CADDIE

CADDIE

With an Introduction by Dymphna Cusack

THE COLLECTOR'S LIBRARY OF
AUSTRALIA'S GREAT BOOKS

Published by
TIMES HOUSE

To
MY MOTHER
A Tribute and a Memorial
and to
TERRY AND ANN

TIMES HOUSE PUBLISHING
61-69 Anzac Parade, Kensington, NSW 2033
Published by arrangement with
Angus & Robertson Publishers

First published 1953
The A&R Australian Classics edition, 1981
This Australia's Great Books edition, 1984
Reprinted 1986, 1987
Copyright 1953 C. A. Wright
Copyright Introduction 1965 Dymphna Cusack
National Library of Australia
Cataloguing-in-publication data
Caddie
    Caddie, a Sydney barmaid
    (Australian classics)
    First published, London: Constable, 1953
ISBN 0 85835 704 6

Printed in Singapore
by Toppan Printing Co.

Introduction

On a bright May Day in 1953, *Caddie – A Sydney Barmaid* was launched on the English market with what publishers called 'rave' reviews in the Press.

It was the triumph of Caddie's life. For the distinguished writer and critic, Michael Sadlier, and for me the book's success confirmed the belief we had had in it from the beginning.

For him that was the day in 1951 I handed him the battered typescript Caddie had sent from Sydney. Although he did not become my publisher until 1954, with *Southern Steel,* a friendship had developed between us from the evening when Florence James and I met him on the B.B.C.'s 'Pacific Newsreel' to discuss the writing of *Come In Spinner.* I had implicit faith in his judgement. He had that quality rare in literary scholars – and he was a distinguished scholar as well as critic – of seeing contemporary writing as a product and expression of its own time, to be judged in modern terms. The wealth of his scholarship enriched his instinct for books, even a book still in the making that an Australian and an English publisher had already rejected.

He believed in *Caddie* from that first reading as I had believed in it through all the years of its making.

For me that went back a long way. For seven years I had watched a potential story-teller progress from the unconnected verbal telling of incidents, through the painful struggle to give them written form – something that provided me with one of the most fascinating experiences of my own literary life.

I first met Caddie on a sparkling morning in March 1945. I didn't realize then, as my friend Florence James and I waited for our new 'help' to arrive, that she was to prove to be much more than the treasure we had dreamed of finding, since we had taken a large ramshackle cottage on the Blue Mountains where we intended to settle down to the writing of *Come in Spinner.*

It had been an alluring dream seen from the city where we'd

both had strenuous war-time jobs which had ended for me with a year in-and-out of hospital. In down-to-earth fact it wasn't so easy. The house was large and old. Bush fires had run through the property just before we moved in, ruining the orchard and leaving only twisted wires where the fence had been. Instead of our shelter of thick bush growth we were perched in a wilderness of scorched earth, charred trees and burnt underbrush so that every stirring of air spread a fine shower of dust and ash and cinders over everything. Then too, three small school girls made a lot of work and no one ever succeeded in disciplining the assorted and ever-increasing family of pet animals – and bantams! – into wiping their feet before they wandered uninvited into the house.

In addition, our romantic country cottage was deplorably lacking in the labour-saving devices we'd taken for granted in Sydney. We needed help. But where to look for it? Domestic help in Australia is hard to get at any time and in 1945, with every spare woman in some sort of war job, it was considered a waste of effort to advertise.

We 'advertised' in the traditional local fashion: that is, we begged the taxi-driver, the milk-woman, the butcher, the baker, the grocer and the fruiterer, when they came with deliveries, to ask on their rounds if anyone knew of anyone –

News came back. There *was* someone who would come and help us, but as she lived on the other side of the scattered village we would have to send a taxi for her. We got in touch with the taxi-driver – inadequate title for a man who played so versatile and vital a role in our little community. The milk-woman (our Fairy Godmother in many ways) took a note for us. We couldn't believe our luck.

And the next Monday morning the taxi drew up with a loud, triumphal honking at our dilapidated back gate (our main entrance). A woman in her mid-forties, plump and trim, got out, carrying a large bunch of beautiful pink dahlias. She smiled at us as she came down the path, a charming picture in her blue and white floral frock, so self-possessed that we were suddenly painfully aware of our far-from-immaculate khaki slacks and shirts.

We introduced ourselves. We explained that we couldn't cope with all the household tasks and get ahead satisfactorily with our writing. We had a cup of tea together and then we fled to our work-rooms with sighs of relief. From the sounds in laundry and kitchen we felt that there was nothing we could tell Caddie that she didn't already know better than we did.

Over lunch we found out something more about our 'treasure'. We found that we owed our amazing luck to the fact that we were writers. She didn't need to go out to work, but, as she wrote to me later: 'You know, I really came to work for you out of curiosity. I'd never before seen an author in the flesh. I'd read about poor, emaciated creatures living in garrets and hawking their manuscripts round and I wanted to see what you were like. Besides, I was bored with mothers' meetings and listening to local gossip. And my son was fighting in the jungle and had at one time been reported missing. I thought I'd have less time to worry.'

Lunch on 'Caddie's days' became an event. We found her interest in writers was not merely of the gossip-column type.

'I'd like to write a book myself,' she used to say, 'but I never had the education.'

I remember the sigh that followed those words.

Then her eyes brightened. 'But I could give you wonderful copy for your stories if you like.'

It was then she began to tell us about the years she had spent as a barmaid. So at lunch time I used to sit with a notebook at my elbow. Caddie spoke racily; she had the gift for a phrase no education can give. I remember the way she told us of one of her 'missuses' in the bar, sitting crouched over the till, 'picking up money greedily like a fowl picking up wheat.' Her comment on a neighbour who professed to be shocked at some small local scandals: 'What would shock her would put a donkey off its oats.' Her description of her initiation as a barmaid, and how eventually she 'learned to pull beer without losing a sud.'

The stories had a dramatic vividness. She brought to life for us the world she had lived in. She told us her own story too, sometimes with passion, sometimes with irony, sometimes with bitterness – a bitterness that was directed at things as they had been rather than at peop' . We were astonished at times that a woman who had suf red so much had so little bitterness in her. She had in some curious fashion the capacity to get outside herself and her own problems. I can see us still, the three of us seated around the lunch table on our verandah, from which the timbered valley and ochre cliffs fell away in a perpetual blue haze to Sydney sixty miles distant. Caddie, with her well-shaped arms resting on the table, her rounded face with its faint tracery of lines under wavy, light brown hair streaked with grey, her mouth that in repose showed the lines of suffering graven deeply at the corners, her grey-blue eyes looking absently over the ruined orchard, the smoke from a cigarette drifting up unheeded as her mind went back selecting, rounding, emphasizing each anecdote in a way the trained writer must envy. She had a flair not only for the phrase but for the significant incident.

Gradually her life took shape for us – the rough and tumble of her childhood days in the raw camp in the bush, the Cinderella marriage, then the long and gallant struggle of a young, untrained woman to rear two children decently.

Without realizing it, in the telling she revealed also her qualities of character. She had fought against odds that would have broken anyone with less spirit, to remain 'respectable' and give her children the chance in life she had never had. To keep herself and her children, she had been forced to take a job in what the evidence of the Royal Commission in 1951-2 disclosed as the most corrupt and corrupting legal occupation Australia knew and knows.

She told us how, as the depression of the thirties settled like a blight over the community, like millions of others on labour-crowded markets, she was forced to accept cut wages and harsh conditions in order to live. She in turn, at the Boss's or Missus's orders, exploited the customers. Dispassionately, she told how she learned all the mean and dirty tricks of the trade.

'Even at the time I despised myself for it,' she said, 'but when a woman has no money and children to keep she can't be fussy about things like that.'

The battle intensified as jobs became difficult to get. The pressure of poverty and near-starvation, the dread of what might happen to her children pushed her deeper and deeper into the struggle, with all the bureaucratic horrors that beset people without money or jobs. 'I did things I never thought I'd do,' she said. 'But when you're down, you can't afford to be finicky.' For month after month we listened to Caddie's experiences.

Against the lawless corrupt background she painted so vividly there gradually emerged a story of a mother's love for her children and her willingness to sacrifice everything for them. Her whole life-struggle was a conflict between her essential decency and an environment that would have debased a woman of lesser quality. For if Caddie's 'professional' life mirrored the growing corruption of a community which admitted no values except making the biggest possible profit, her personal story revealed the incredible strength of an essentially decent human being who wins through eventually to temporary security for herself and her children by her skill and daring in a second profession – this (crowning irony) outside the Law – as an 'S.P. bookie'.

Against the background of Blue Mountain valleys that gradually came to life again after the devastation of the bush fires, her life unfolded itself.

There was something symbolic about that landscape with its indescribable quality of timelessness, the blackened gum-trees putting out new spring leaves of translucent ruby and garnet, the wattles rioting in showers of gold, the ti-tree trailing its veils of snowy blossom, and all the native scrub showing its capacity to endure, to survive, to grow and bloom again.

She told her story factually, explaining how she had grown a special 'skin' to enable her to deal with the problems of her life as a barmaid. But in her essential humility she saw only the 'skin' and not the woman who had come to maturity beneath it. Now, freed from external pressure she realized her material was dramatic, but she never thought herself capable of using it.

One day she gave us the plot of a play she would like to write, based on an incident out of her own life, the kind of incident an author would scarcely dare invent for fear of being shouted down for extravagance, melodrama, overstraining the excessively long arm of coincidence. It was the way she told that story that made us realize, with a shock, that Caddie was not only an apparently inexhaustible mine of material but potentially a writer herself. Of this play, she wrote to me later: 'I sincerely wanted you to use it. But you both cried me down. You would not hear of it. It was *my* idea, you said, and I must try to write the play myself. You both told me you had faith in me. You were confident I could do it. It was on the strength of your faith in me and the influence you had come to exert over me that I finally decided to give it a go. Somehow your opinion mattered to me a great deal. I wanted to sort of live up to it. So I began to write my little play. I spent one winter on it here in this very room. I used to switch off the light and sit before a lovely log fire dreaming it and scribbling it on a pad on my knee. The characters came to life. They lived with me. I grew to love them. It was a most fascinating experience.'

'Caddie's days' now became more than washing and cleaning and listening to her reminiscences. There was the play to discuss and she swept through the work like a whurly-whurly to have a longer lunch hour for talking it over. Gradually it took form. It was finished. Then Caddie in her generosity offered us all the rich tumultuous material that she had gathered in her life – to write. In a letter written years later when she sent me the final draft of the autobiography of a barmaid, she said:

'You'll remember how you both dogged me to start on the story myself. I remember one afternoon just as I was about to leave, you and Florence got to work on me, challenging me that I was not to come back again unless I had made a start on my story. You thrust a large book into my hands saying: "Here you are. Now get going on it!" I opened the book. It had ruled lines and on the inside cover you had written in purple ink: "To Caddie. Now go to it!" and underneath, "Dymphna Cusack, 16/1/47." I put the book in my bag and looking at you both I said rather solemnly: "Yes, I'll write it. At least I'll get it on the paper if it is the last thing I ever do." But on the way home I said to myself: "Now, how the hell am I going to do it?" I wondered if you two girls back there really knew what you were letting yourselves in for, seeing you had both promised to act as critics for me. After reading over the first draft you will never believe me when I tell you how I sweated over it. As I watched you crawl through it!' ('Crawl' it was, for Caddie's handwriting wasn't too easy to read) 'I was seized with an impulse to snatch it out of your hands. I felt strangely self-conscious as though I were standing naked before you, that you were looking into my soul.'

Poor Caddie! You didn't know that every writer, no matter how experienced, feels that same creeping of the flesh and the spirit the first time the new story is read by another. But for you it was more than a story. It was your own life you were trying to put on paper and, as you said yourself, 'It just wouldn't jell.' You, whose speech was so racy and entertaining found that somewhere in the translation into the written word the savour was lost. You distrusted your own racy idiom. You couldn't believe that was what we wanted on paper. You shrank from revealing your own reactions to events in your life. What you didn't know, you whose whole literary experience consisted of a half-hour play, was that each of us goes through that agonizing moment. I have often thought as I

x

have read over a chapter put down at white heat that the finished product couldn't be mine, there was so little relation between that brief, exciting flare in my mind and the cold soddenness of the written word.

I remember how, when I was a child, I used to lie outstretched at the sea's edge and watch the busy life in the rock pools. The tiny flashing fish, the flickering anemone, the scuttling crabs, the pebbles glittering like jewels in the reflected light. How often I've watched a pebble, gloating over its iridescence, fancying there was a vein of gold through it, thinking how beautiful it would look if I took it home and put it on my table. I can remember the cool shock of the water as I plunged my arm in, the shiver as the tentacles of the anemone touched my skin, the prickling of my scalp as I fumbled in water suddenly full of swirling sand. Maybe there was a baby octopus under the rocks, maybe. . . . The groping, the slippery stone eluding my fingers, then triumph. But triumph that didn't last. The stone that, seen through the water was a jewel, in my hand was only another pebble growing rapidly duller as the water dried on it.

Caddie had to learn everything from the beginning. We pointed out to her that she had only touched the surface of the story as told to us. She had omitted many interesting incidents, characters she had talked of, events she had described, her own reflections on her life as she had lived it – all this must go in.

After a long discussion and criticism of the manuscript she started again. I always feel that the test of a potential writer is the ability to go back to a manuscript when the glow of creation has faded.

Then came the next draft which wasn't merely a string of disconnected incidents. Event and character began to take shape. Oh, the agony of that manuscript both in the writing and the reading! Caddie's handwriting got more illegible as she became more fluent. I remember groaning as I tried to decipher some of the packed pages: 'Oh, Caddie, I wish you could type!'

Next time she came she made the staggering announcement that she had hired a typewriter (you couldn't buy a typewriter at that time in Australia), and was teaching herself to type 'to make it easier for you to read'.

I felt humble. When you face such courage and determination all your own defects rise up and shame you.

Full of excitement, Caddie went on: 'I began by using one finger then after a while I found myself using both hands, and now I can go a bit faster. But, oh the mistakes!'

Draft Three was slowly re-done in typescript. In the meantime Florence left for England, I went back to my city home and it was six months before I saw Caddie again. I think she can tell that part of the story best herself:

'I sent you Draft Three and sat back and waited. You wrote to say you'd be coming to a friend in the Mountains again in the near future for a couple of weeks to collect some material you wanted for *Say No to Death*. When you had a free moment, I must come over for lunch and we'd discuss the story. You'll never know how anxiously I waited for that invitation. It came at last. I found you in a quaint little cottage in the bush. You came down the path to meet me and I'm sure you didn't know that my knees were knocking together for fear of what your verdict would be. We sat down in the tiny living room and I watched you as you arranged the flowers I'd brought.

'Funny how things like that stay in your mind, your suntanned hands moving among the flowers, while I sat with my heart going tick-tock . . . waiting. Then over a cup of tea we discussed the story. We went through it chapter by chapter and you had written practically a page-by-page criticism. Once more you urged me to put in some of the things I'd told you about but had omitted to write. I noticed that in our many discussions on my book you never once told me to take anything out of it. You advised me how to try and organize it better, how to tidy it up. I looked at the pages of suggestions and my heart went into my boots for I realized it meant another re-writing. But you said you'd be leaving for England in about six months time and I knew that if I didn't get it done by then. . . . So I set to work again in a fury of concentration and when I'd finished I took it to you, this time in your Sydney flat that looked out on to the lovely little bay at Kirribilli. "Surely," I said to myself as I walked up the hill from the ferry, "surely this is the last time." '

I opened the door to Caddie bearing her familiar burdens, a huge bunch of flowers from her mountain garden, a bag crammed with home-grown vegetables and a delicious cooked chicken. It was not till afterwards that she confessed that she felt that day that she simply couldn't tackle the MS again whatever I said. If she had known there were to be still two more drafts, she'd probably never have come at all.

It seemed inhuman to insist, for Caddie, with an eye to collecting material for a story about delinquent girls, had taken a job that used up most of her energies. She was cooking for sixty girls at a factory hostel.

Only afterwards did I realize just how hard she worked those last months. 'As soon as I've finished my day's work,' she wrote to me later, 'I go straight to my little cottage about 100 yards from the main building and, after a quick shower, sit down at the typewriter and get going. It's a case of work, work and more work.'

Gallant Caddie! Unhappily for her that day I was in the mood of clinical vivisection I bring to my own final drafts. And I was demanding from her in the writing of her own life what I would expect from myself in the writing of fiction: the story in the round, incident in suspense, emotion motivating action and character determining event. I wanted the whole of that rich, vital, generous personality on paper – and written by a beginner! I wanted others to see her as I saw her: Caddie, who had come through twenty years of a life most women would find completely degrading, upheld in poverty and despair by her passionate love for her children; saved from personal corruption by her essential and incorruptible decency; Caddie, who had been to all superficial appearance only a pawn in the social conflict and who emerged from the conflict a strong and honest woman. Caddie, who had endured the humiliation of struggling to obtain relief rights that were given as reluctantly as though they were charity, and kept her pride.

Over the lunch table we thrashed out what must be done in the next draft. For the first time Caddie demurred. She didn't see how she could do anything more to it. It was finished.

'It's not finished,' I said. 'You've got to make the blood flow, the nerves tingle.'

Caddie rested an aching head on a hand red from the kitchen. She was tired, and the thermometer was in the 90's and she had to be back to cook the dinner. Maybe she thought I sounded theatrical. 'You'll have to put more feeling in it. Think what you'd feel yourself if you met a woman in your position.'

I looked at her across the table – at the rounded face on which suffering and struggle had etched their lines. At the eyes that could be humorous, kind, hard. Suddenly the quiet-faced woman became for me a symbol of all the women who battle against the handicaps that nature and society have imposed on them. I saw the child she had been, riding wildly through the night and the storm to get a doctor for her mother. I saw the girl who wanted to 'improve herself', the bewildered girl-wife caught up in a mesh of psychological and personal problems she hadn't the wisdom to sort out, the inexperienced woman against the world or – perhaps it would be truer to say – with the world against her. I wanted other people to be torn as I'd been torn when she told me the story. 'Yes, you must do it again,' I insisted, 'and this time you mustn't play down the hardships in your life. You mustn't shrink from revealing your reactions to the things that happened to you.'

Caddie stared at me for a while without speaking, frowning, obviously turning over things in her mind. Then she began to talk slowly as though an entirely new idea had been presented to her. 'I don't see what you mean about playing down hardships. It's the truth. The only time I've deliberately changed anything is where the truth might hurt people who weren't responsible for what happened. I see no point in hurting them.'

I started to say that truth isn't enough in a *novel* and stopped, remembering that this isn't a novel. It is a *life*. 'Here you are with the story of a lifetime,' I burst out. 'You haven't to invent anything. Think of your children.' The light of battle came into her eyes and I hurried on, 'think of what they suffered.'

We sat looking at each other. Her eyes filled with tears. There was a lump in my throat.

The tears glistened in Caddie's eyes, and I knew she was seeing over the years the picture I saw. I had a feeling of triumph. At last I had broken down her defences. 'Think of what you suffered for them,' I begged.

She continued to look at me but her face changed. 'It was worth it.'

'I'm not questioning that but . . .'

'Any woman would have done what I did.'

'You know that's not true,' I insisted.

'Well,' she conceded, 'perhaps some women who are good enough mothers at ordinary times do drop their bundle when things go wrong, and part with their children either by adopting them out or dumping them in a home and forgetting them. But most women in my position would stick to their children no matter how tough things were.'

I knew I'd lost but I made a last effort. 'But Caddie, surely you can see that yours is a heart-breaking story. You've got to make people feel that.'

'I never pulled a poor mouth in my life.'

'But this is different. If you can make them feel sorry for you –'

She looked me straight in the eyes, an expression of immovable obstinacy settled on her face. 'I don't want to be pitied,' she said flatly. 'I loathe it. I never asked for pity in my life and I'm not going to start now.'

She did two more drafts. The first came to me in England in 1950. I went through it, scrawled suggestions all over it and sent it back to her. I wonder now how I could have been so demanding.

It came again in 1951 with a flat statement: 'Take it or leave it. I can't do another thing to it.'

It was not yet ready for publication, but in spite of its roughness I knew it was good. I sent it to Michael Sadlier. He read it over the week-end.

Looking at me over his half-moon glasses when we met on the following Tuesday his opening remark was: 'Smashing!' (For all his rich vocabulary he loved a touch of slang.) 'It's alive! It's real! We'll publish it if you'll write an introduction and get it into publishing form – if Caddie is willing.'

Caddie wrote: 'Do what you like with it. In a way it's been your baby from the beginning.'

So, during the winter of 1952 I set to work on the editing of the script and the writing of the introduction in the sun-trap that is Menton-Garavan on the Cote d' Azur.

Caddie wrote to me when she signed the contract:

'I can't tell you how happy I am. First the exciting news that my story is going to be published. And then Mother's Day this year has been a wonderful celebration for me. Ann came to see us with her little daughter who looks just like she did when I first went to work in a pub. Then Terry arrived with a beautiful new typewriter for me – a portable, cream with nickel fittings he had bought out of his war gratuity. It was a great surprise. I hadn't told them that the book had been accepted, I was saving it up till I saw them – which makes his lovely gift all the nicer. They were as thrilled as I was when they heard the news. What a day we had together! Didn't I once tell you that anything I went through for my children was worth it? Well, it was!

'Only one shadow. I was very sad when I got a letter from Pat the other day telling me that Bill Sutton had died in Concord Military Hospital from injuries received while a prisoner-of-war. I looked at my Terry and thought: How lucky I am.

'Goodbye for now and God bless.'

In May 1953, *Caddie – A Sydney Barmaid* was published by Constable & Co. Over a lunch Michael and I gloated over the reviews.

Storm Jameson wrote: 'It is a fine, brave book, intensely and continuously interesting, one of those very rare books which do administer a salutary shock to the reader's mind as well as engaging his heart. It impressed me enormously.'

And Nancy Spain: 'A moving and most human story. . . . Her description of city life among the poor is terrifying. But Caddie fights through it all. Hers is a success story that will make you proud to be a human being. Through loneliness, despair, corruption, hunger and terror she battles like a tiger with her children behind her.'

Ten thousand miles away Caddie shared our jubilation in the cabled Press reports of her book's reception which plunged her suddenly into the limelight. By pure chance its publication followed the exposures by the Royal Commission on Liquor in New South Wales and appeared as a personal case-history to the biggest post-war scandal in Australia.

By September the book had been reprinted three times. *Caddie,* the Barmaid was famous but not the woman who wrote it. Her name appeared only on the contract. She shrank from publicity. Nobody but those intimately connected with the book and its writing knew who she was or where she was. There were even rumours that Caddie was my invention!

It was only when I came home from China in 1958 that I persuaded her to come to the Fellowship of Writers' reception and introduced her, at her own request, by the only name she wished to bear as a public figure, Caddie.

And here is her story, the story of a woman who endured hardship and exploitation, the loss of her loved ones by betrayal and by death, and who, even in retrospect did not want to be pitied.

DYMPHNA CUSACK

October 1965

xvi

1

I was twenty-four when I got my first job in a Sydney hotel bar, not from choice, but because I was broke and needed the money to support myself and my two young children. I can remember that day as though it was yesterday. It was the first time in my life that I'd been in a bar. In 1924, not only was it forbidden by law for women to drink in a bar, but no woman who valued her reputation would have dared put her nose even into a Ladies' Parlour. To most respectable Australians a barmaid was beyond the pale. Indeed I felt that morning as I took my place behind the long counter – imagining every eye on me – that I had put myself on the outer. Not that I really had any choice.

I remember feeling sick with shame as one old fellow, his face a bright scarlet, grinned as the landlady introduced me to the customers and called out:

'Good looking sheila you got there' and another added – 'I see you're still goin' fer the young stuff, Missus', and all the men guffawed as though he'd said something screamingly funny.

The landlady ignored them, but my hands were shaking as I picked up a towel and began to rinse and dry a trayful of soiled glasses under the counter.

It's strange how a place will stay in your mind like a photograph. I can still see that bar, though I couldn't keep track of all the bars I've worked in since.

It was oblong, the shelves beneath the counter stacked with glasses upside down and of various sizes, laid out on white Turkish towelling, similar to that used for babies' nappies. I know it sounds silly and sentimental, but the sight of that towelling nearly made me burst out crying, then and there, for the home I'd lost and the plight my babies and I had come to. Not that I liked washing babies' nappies more than anyone else. But they'd meant home and – so I once thought – love and security. But it was no time and no place for tears – I could cry at home. Customers expect a bright face, and their troubles were more important to them than mine.

That morning I stood choking down the lump in my throat and trying to find out where things were.

The lower shelves were filled with bottled beer and stout, whilst on an overhead shelf running parallel to the counter were rows of cordials and bottles of wines and spirits of all kinds. At the end of this shelf stood two small kegs, one marked Rum and the other Wine. Yes, just Wine. It was filled with cheap port, I found out later. A cash register stood on a desk well back from the counter. Two groups of beer-taps jutted out from the woodwork and under them were shiny driptrays. In the floor was a trapdoor leading to the cellar, fitted with an iron ring. The walls around the bar were covered with mirrors which carried advertisements for various brands of beers and whiskies.

I took all this in as I went on rinsing and drying glasses. Two of the men began to play cards with a pack borrowed from the landlady whose name was Mrs Smith. The others went on talking, not bothering to lower their voices. One of them was telling a tall story and I was startled to hear the other say –

'You be buggered. I won't have that.'

I expected trouble but quickly saw that it was merely doubt, stated with emphasis. And I realized, at the same time, that my father's idea that a man didn't swear in front of a woman didn't hold in public bars. Nor apparently did it matter what kind of jokes were told in front of a barmaid. I was blushing to the roots of my hair by the time the men, with the exception of a chap named Bluey and the card players, drained their glasses and walked out.

A loud guffaw came from one of the cards players as he banged his hairy hand on the counter. Apparently the loser had to shout and when the winner called for drinks, the landlady told me to serve them. I went over and politely asked them what they were having. The spokesman ignored me, looking over my head to call the landlady to serve them, but she ignored him and walked to the far end of the bar. I felt embarrassed and when he realized Mrs Smith was not going to serve them, he looked at me and said:

'I'll have a portergaff – and a beer straight.'

Bewildered, I picked up two glasses and turned to walk along to the beer taps. As I did so, Mrs Smith moved up to me and said quietly that they were not the right glasses. She showed me those I should use, and pointed to an unopened bottle of stout and a bottle of lemonade, saying:

'Just a dash of stout.'

Unfortunately, I handled the bottle too roughly, disturbing the lively liquor so that, when the stopper fell to the flour, the stout spurted all over my dress and shoes. Mrs Smith took the bottle from me and putting the neck well down in the glass, and to one side, expertly poured the required drink. The two card players were highly amused, and their laughter made me nervous. I felt like a kid at a new school. New school was right! These men were aware that I was new to the game and instead of giving their order in a way I would understand had deliberately confused me.

But the day came when I could handle those drinks without losing a drop. The day came, too, when I could handle punks like those two card players. However, that day was a long way off. Then I could only stand, angry and ashamed of my mistake, trying to mop the stout off my frock, hating the smell of it, hating the silly half-shot loafers who had nothing better to do than stand there watching me make a fool of myself.

All the misery of the past months boiled up in me. What would my mother have thought if she could have known that her daughter had come down to serving in a public bar – my mother, whom no hardships, no crudity of life could make forget that she was a respectable woman and who, for good reasons, hated everything connected with the drink trade.

What would my mother-in-law think? Probably that it proved that she had been right from the beginning in her dislike of me! She had always thought I wasn't good enough for her son. And what would the son think? Well, he could scarcely think less of me than he did or I wouldn't have been there at all.

I badly wanted to turn and run out of the bar, away from the grins of the customers. But I remembered that I'd have to get some money somehow and this job would get me more than any other I knew.

How did I, a married woman with two young children, come to be a barmaid when I was obviously unsuited to the job? For as I look back no one could have been less suited than I. At first I suppose I was a bit of a prig. I know now I was a prude. I had my mother's attitude to drink. I'd never taken a glass of intoxicating liquor, and I clung as fiercely as she did to the decent things of life. *

3

When you have had to battle as my mother battled and I battled you know it really means something to keep respectable. I hadn't had an easy life. Indeed, when I married John Marsh, at the end of the first World War when he was twenty-four and I was eighteen, my marriage seemed like Cinderella's story brought up to date.

I look back on that first day in the bar as one remembers a nightmare. Everything larger than life and slightly out of focus. I suppose the fact is that everything in my life at the time made me abnormally sensitive: The loss of my husband in such a cruel way, worry for children left in the care of a woman I didn't trust and, overhanging everything, the fear that every woman has when she has children dependent on her. What if I got ill? What would happen to my children, if – ? But in actual fact, that day I had little time to bother about 'if's' – I was too busy.

Apart from serving in the bar it was my job to look after the Ladies' Parlour, two back rooms well away from the bar, specially fitted out with tables and chairs for those females who liked their drop. It was necessary to pass through the room nearest the street to enter the second which, lacking windows, was always musty and stifling. This latter I was to discover was, by some unwritten law, the special reserve of the older women who drank mainly wine and spirits, having reached the stage, apparently, where nothing weaker could give them the necessary kick. The other room was the haunt of the younger women, the beer and gin drinkers, and the passing trade – strangers dropping in for a drink, who were tolerated, but watched with suspicion by the regulars.

Many of the drinkers were young girls and occasionally a pregnant woman.

The Missus explained to me that a lot of glasses were broken or stolen, and I was to go into the parlour frequently, rescuing empty glasses from the tables or floor.

Getting into this crowd was one thing, but getting out was another. They were all interested in the new barmaid and wanted to get on the good side of her. I was mobbed by women, pawed by the men who occasionally came with their missuses or their women, some just good-natured, others drunk and sentimental.

As time went on I got to know them well enough to call them by their Christian names and I got along all right with most of them. But that day they repelled me, with their

alcohol-laden breath, their meaningless profanity, their care-
lessness of their appearance. However, when I went in to
gather empty glasses and wipe down the tables, one or other
of them would call out, ' 'Ow are yer kid? Y'gunna 'ave a
drink?' and 'Gorn, lovey, 'ave one with me.' When I told
them I didn't drink in working hours they insisted on me
accepting the money, saying, 'Well, 'ave one after, luv.' This
money went into a glass the Missus advised me to keep near
the till for tips.

To carry a tray load of drinks through this rowdy throng
was out of the question; drinks were served through a servery
built into the door leading from the bar to the parlour.

Late that afternoon the usual noise from the parlour suddenly increased, and was punctuated by screams and the
crash of breaking glass. The Missus called the useful to take
over. A fight had started in the front parlour and women were
biting and scratching in one mad mix up, knocking tables
over and wiping glasses to the floor. The useful was not in the
race to stop them, but knowing from long experience what
would happen if the trouble spread to the back parlour, he
stood near the communicating door to stop the brawlers from
passing in, or any of the older women from coming out. The
front-roomers merely engaged in a bout of hair-pulling and
scratching, but the back-roomers, when stirred, so the Missus
told me, usually favoured the broken glass or bottle as their
weapon. I was to learn that a beer glass, held by the base, and
the lip broken off sharply against a table, is probably the
nastiest weapon after the razor.

The Missus had rung for the police at the first sign of
trouble. They arrived quickly. Used to this routine they had
brought a Black Maria, parking it outside the parlour door.
They led out the tractable contestants, the more violent ones
being carried out, struggling and kicking, screaming threats
at the police, the boss, and each other. A police sergeant
walked through and ordered the remaining customers from
the parlour, telling the boss to close the doors.

The police departed, leaving a group of women standing
outside the pub, calling out their opinions of the mug coppers,
and that dirty bitch in there, meaning the Missus. Several
poked their heads into the public bar, calling out to men they
knew to pass a drink out to them, but the Missus put the
kibosh on them. 'You can't drink in the street. Do you want
to get pinched?"

5

One big blousy woman kicked the door wide open and forced her way through the men lining the counter. Throwing herself half over the counter she snarled at the useful: 'You, ya dirty bugger, ya bloody mean bastard. That's what I think of you. And as for that dirty old slut there! – ' she pointed to the Missus, and proceeded to describe her, drawing on a vocabulary as colourful as any I ever heard in later years. She swore for what seemed to my shocked ears, many minutes. I was numb with fear and loathing. Some of the men around the bar looked at her in disgust, while others showed their admiration at her range of bad language. The Missus sat at the till unconcerned. Then suddenly she picked up the receiver from the telephone and said, 'Are you going, or will I call the police?'

At this one of the customers called out from the other side of the bar: 'Go on, Daise, beat it before she gets the coppers.'

Daise was nobody's fool. She left with a last burst of brilliant profanity directed at the Missus. The women outside jammed every door to hear their champion, and they withdrew as she left, moving away to seek out a parlour elsewhere to round off their afternoon. I'd never heard women swear like that in my life. I was sickened as well as shocked. But I had no time to worry about it.

Soon the six o'clock rush was in full swing. It was a long time before I learned to handle that evening rush with any degree of skill. The beer foamed over the tops of the glasses, men complained of 'too much collar on it'. The first arrivals crowded against the counter, less fortunate ones called above their heads, late comers jostled and shouted and swore in an attempt to be served before closing time.

It was a revolting sight and one it took a long time for me to take for granted. The smell of liquor, the smell of human bodies, the warm smell of wine, and on one early occasion even a worse smell, as a man, rather than give up his place at the counter, urinated against the bar. We were all flat out serving – the useful, the Missus, the casual barman who came in only at peak hours, and myself. My head was splitting, my feet were killing me.

The shouting for service, the crash of falling glasses, the grunting and shoving crowd, and that loud, indistinguishable clamour of conversation found nowhere but in a crowded bar beat in on my brain until all my actions became mechanical. Suddenly there was a crash as a stool was knocked over, and I looked up to see a scuffling movement in one corner of the bar. Quickly the crowd drew away from the corner, to reveal two men wrestling and punching each other in fury, as each tried to spin the other to the floor. It lasted only a minute or so, as several of the crowd grabbed each of the men and held them apart. Soon they were back at the counter, each with his group of listeners gathered about him, and each giving similar descriptions of what he would have done to the other, if 'you'se blokes hadn't broke it up'.

I asked old Bluey, who had stood and watched it all with a grin, what had started it. 'Ar, the clown in the blue shirt tried ter take the other joker's beer, and got caught – that's all.'

I went home exhausted. I really believe that if I could have thought of any other job at all that I could do that would bring me in as much, I'd have given up barmaiding then and there. But there wasn't. And in addition to my salary, I'd made a few shillings in tips.

I put the children to bed, too tired even to get a meal for myself. I stank of beer. Terry pulled away from me when I went to kiss him and complained that I smelled like Mrs Platt. I soaked myself and my clothes in a hot bath – then I went to sleep to dream of an endless succession of public bars at peak hour.

2

My torment at my first bar experiences will be better understood if I give some account of my family and particularly of my mother and of my early life.

I was born at the turn of the century at Penrith, a small town about thirty miles west of Sydney, which sprawled untidily almost at the foot of the Blue Mountains. It was a dreary place, scorching heat in the summer and bitter cold in the winter. My mother's parents came from Scotland in the eighties and settled at Penrith, where my grandfather owned the local flour mills and quite a lot of property.

Both my grandparents' families owned cotton mills in Scotland and were supposed to be somebodies. The old fashioned photo album had the proof of grandmother's statement that her father rode to hounds and they had their monogram on their carriage, for what that was worth!

My grandfather was given a large sum of money by his father just before leaving his homeland. His mother gave him her blessing and the family Bible.

I believed and still believe my grandmother's boasting, which my mother repeated. My mother's strict upbringing made her have a horror of lying. I never knew her to lie. And despite her unfortunate marriage to my father she retained her – gentility is the only word I can think of to explain what I mean. She carried herself with dignity all through life, no mean feat in the circumstances in which she constantly found herself after linking up with my father.

My grandparents lived in a large stone house on the outskirts of the town, about half a mile from the little, grey-slabbed cottage in which Timothy and I were born. Because my grandfather's home was so large and had some sort of a tower or turret, some one dubbed it The Castle, and the name stuck. It was always referred to as The Castle.

Both my grandparents were noted for being mean, and although they could have well afforded to pay someone to help in the home they would not hear of it, which meant that my mother had to do all the chores, which included all the household tasks as well as milking the cows. Yet no expense was spared where their younger daughter Prissy was concerned. She had been delicate from birth. She spent much of her time reclining on a couch before a window that was never closed for it was believed that she was suffering from lung trouble.

My father's background was very different. He lost his parents in Ireland and at the age of twelve stowed away on a windjammer and landed at Circular Quay, Sydney. There he joined up with a Scottish lad about his own age, and together they sold papers in Sydney around Circular Quay. They had no home and slept in doorways.

After a while he came to Penrith and worked as a stable boy for my grandfather, later to become a timber cutter for one of his mills at twenty-five shillings a week.

The first bloom of youth had passed for my mother when she decided to marry my father. Perhaps she felt it was her last chance, perhaps she wanted to get away from home because she was tired of being an unpaid servant, or perhaps she really loved my father and nothing else mattered. Whatever it was, my mother would never talk about it.

One night they took a horse from the stable and rode into Penrith and got married. When her father found out there was a rumpus. He never had any time for the big Irishman, but I think it was more the loss of the cheap household drudge he had made of my mother than affection that upset him.

Timothy was mother's first child. Timothy resembled mother. His jet black hair was thick and wavy and his eyes were of the same blue. He was two years older than I, but looked younger, so everyone said. Perhaps it was because he was a premature baby; whereas I had stayed the distance only to make a hurried entry by being born in my mother's petticoats while my father took the horse and dray and drove as fast as the draught mare would go in an effort to get Mary Rawler, the town's one and only midwife.

Timothy was a serious little fellow and was mother's favourite. I was strong-willed, and would have *my* say. I was afraid of no one except my father. Both Timothy and I feared him. He certainly was hard to get along with. He was a grafter* and worked out in the bush six days a week.

Saturday nights Dad would take a bath in the round iron tub in the lean-to at the back of the house, put on a clean shirt and join his mates at the Red Cow; a pub at Penrith station. (I never thought I'd come to pulling beer for men like him one day!)

Saturday nights we feared most. Dad would return home about eleven o'clock, and pity help us if he happened to be in a bad humour. We always knew what sort of a temper he would be in. If he came along singing – we could hear him half a mile away – it was a safe bet that things would be O.K. But if on the other hand he came in quietly we could be prepared for anything. He did such things as throwing the lighted kerosene lamp against the wall, or ordering us out of the house.

When he did these things Mum would grab Timothy and calling to me to follow, would beat a quick retreat, for she was just as afraid of him as we were.

We often slept out in the paddock, the two of us huddled against my mother for warmth, our faces and clothing wet with the dew. Sometimes when everything was quiet we would creep back and, provided my father was snoring his head off, we would all get into the little bed in the back room.

It might be thought that my mother would go home to her

* In Australia a grafter is a very hard worker.

9

parents for shelter and protection. She never did. Her father had in fact, although not in word, disowned her the day she got married.

As time went on it seemed that I was the only one who could manage my father when he came home drunk.

Many times have I been wakened by my mother, standing at my bedside in her nightdress holding a candle, her two long braids of hair unravelled forming two beautiful curls. She would say urgently, 'Wake up! Hurry! It's your father!'

The urgency in her voice would galvanize me into action. I would spring out of bed and hurriedly pull my dress over my shirt. Sometimes I would only be half awake. Then as my father staggered in, I would put on my act. I would greet him with a welcoming smile as though I was awfully pleased to see him, fuss over him, get him a chair, give him his supper; pull off his boots while he began eating and even fill his pipe for him. He in turn would sing for me (he had a lovely tenor voice) sad Irish airs; or he would tell me tales of his adventures. They were most colourful and he told them well. Meantime my mother would have kept out of the way. Sometimes she would take Timothy for a walk, and sometimes she would go to the little back room where Timothy and I used to sleep.

I used to enjoy these little sessions with my father as it was about the only time I could get close to him, for I craved love and affection. And to me at that time love and affection were even more important than a full stomach. Besides, I took pride in looking after him on Saturday nights, for I knew that I was helping my mother. It kept his mind off other things such as picking a quarrel with her for no reason at all. He would hurl insults at her regarding 'them there stuck-up bunch up at The Castle'. He would shout that her parents were sent out for misdeeds in the Old Country; that they did not pay their own fares out; that the government paid them, etc., and other things which were quite false.

Yet although he abused her family I never once heard her say one wrong word about his background.

Sometimes Mum would fondle Timothy, and I would move over to her shyly and lean against her knee or the arm of her chair. More often than not she would push me gently away from her saying playfully: 'Go away, you funny little thing, you don't belong here; the gipsies left you on our doorstep.'

I suppose she meant me to take it in good part, but I was a lonely child and longed for affection. I used to envy other kids who had a good home life and affection.

Everyone in the district liked my mother and some of them gave her their old cast-off clothes. Some of these would fit Timothy and me. We would wear them to school. I remember I was awfully sensitive about wearing other people's things even before I was ten.

Many times some child more fortunate would, with childish thoughtlessness, cruelly point to me before a group of other girls and say, 'Look! she's wearing my old dress'. I would feel the colour come into my face, and turn away so they would not see the tears of shame come into my eyes. It happened to Timothy too.

My father was a great eater. Mum said he needed to be as he worked hard. Timothy and I were never allowed to sit at the table while Dad was having his meal. We had to sit on the floor – there were only two chairs – with our backs against the wall and well away from the fire. We daren't make a sound. Dad sat close to the hearth all the time. We would sit there as quiet as mice watching him eating, our mouths watering for some of the juicy steak he put away. We were never allowed to have meat. I remember Mum rarely sat down with him, she always seemed too busy waiting on him.

She usually had her meal with us. When he was finished he would get up from the table and drag his chair closer towards the hearth, or he would sometimes stand with his back to the fire and watch us as we ate. It depended on what sort of a mood he happened to be in, whether we would get a dressing down, or whether the meal would go off smoothly. On very rare occasions he would joke a little but not often. He used to pound into us so much about what he did for us, that at that age I really believed him. We should both be grateful to him for our daily bread, potatoes, gravy and dripping. We got no butter, that was for him. He had to work hard and needed it.

He was jealous of Timothy and me where Mum was concerned. He hated to see her doing little things for us, like helping us with our lessons. He invariably found some pretext to take her away from us by getting her to do a little job for him, or sometimes carting her off to bed.

He was very good with horses and people used to bring him horses to break in. Sometimes he would give me riding lessons. I had to ride bare-back. As some of the horses were wild I had many a fall. Then he would make me get straight on the horse's back again until I could manage to keep my seat.

He'd whip a horse from behind, and it would bolt. I used to be terrified, but stuck it out as I wanted him to see that I could make the grade. Finally I became a very good rider.

3

When I look back on it, I realize what self-contained children Timothy and I were. We weren't allowed to mix with the children we lived among and the ones Mum thought good enough for us looked down on us. We entertained ourselves. We were never allowed to keep any pets. We were too poor to buy any toys to speak of, so we had to make our own pleasures. We spent as much time as we could out in the open, and loved exploring the bush where we built cubby houses out of bark and branches.

There were never any birthdays or celebrations, except when Dad celebrated in his own particular way. We knew they celebrated up at The Castle at Xmas, but we were never invited. So on Xmas Eve, I would take Timothy by the hand and we would run along the bush track to our grandparents' home. There we would leg up on to the fence and get ourselves a good pozzie with a view of the dining-room. As the weather was always warm the French doors would be wide open. There we would see what was to us a fairyland. A huge Xmas tree loaded with gifts, holly and tinsel, the table spread with a snowy cloth and laden with goodies. As the sun sank Emily, the little maid of all work, would begin to light candles and would pull the blinds. Then we'd go home.

We hung our socks up on Xmas Eve. In the morning there might be a small mechanical toy for Timothy, and a tiny china doll for me and also a paper bag of lollies each. We both believed in Father Xmas all right, but what worried me was why some children got such expensive toys. It seemed to me that Santa Claus had his favourites.

About this time, my grandfather lost nearly all he had in some speculation and went bankrupt. They went to live in a smaller house, and Emily, the little maid who had taken my mother's place at The Castle, was sacked. Aunt Prissy, seeing her easy life ended, immediately married one of her old suitors, and in time bore ten healthy sons. There was nothing wrong with her!

Grandfather's insolvency gave Dad a new topic with which to taunt Mum even though it was not as good as the old ones. About this time Dad lost his job as a timber cutter and took a new one with the Government Railways on the construction of a duplicate line over the Blue Mountains. It was to be a long job and he had to camp along the line, which meant that he could come home only once a fortnight. What a break that was for us!

It was a queer sort of life we led but through all the realities of our poverty and my father's brutality, my mother's firmness in clinging to her belief in what a lady should and should not do, never wavered. She mightn't be able to alter her surroundings but at least she could prevent herself from being overwhelmed by them. And she did. We might have to live on bread and dripping but our table manners were as important as if we'd been sitting down to a feast. We might have to wear other people's cast-offs but they were always clean and neatly patched.

Dad might rave and storm at her but she never replied, and her silence was a kind of criticism in itself. Other children might use swear words and slang, but not hers. Because of her attitude to things that were taken for granted by people we lived among, we never seemed to belong.

Probably that was the reason that the fairy stories and adventure books I read seemed so much more real to me than the life I was living. I was in turn each of the heroines I read about, so that when just about my tenth birthday, Penrith woke one morning to find that a travelling dramatic show was to visit the town I was enchanted. The billboards told us that they were going to put on a play called 'East Lynne'. It would show four nights before moving on to the next town.

I was dying to see real live actors and actresses. I haunted the railway platform when they were due to arrive. There was no mistaking the troupe as they stepped off the train. They were dressed in showy clothes and they must have looked comical, but I thought they were *it*. I offered to help them carry their bags to the nearest hotel, which was the Red Cow. They were amused at me wanting to help, and asked me my name. When I'd done my job, one of them, a fat man who later on I found played the part of the butler in the play, gave me sixpence. Very reluctantly I went home.

But they hadn't seen the last of me. Next afternoon straight after school, I found my way backstage at the main hall. The door was slightly ajar, I pushed it open and went in. They were busy rehearsing, but didn't seem to mind my interrupting them; in fact they seemed pleased to see me. They invited me to sit in the front row while they continued the rehearsal. As I sat and watched I was fascinated: this was right up my alley. I wanted to be an actress! How I loved it, it was wonderful.

I watched Mrs Carlyle as she leant over a table that was covered with a sheet, which was bolstered up with pillows to represent little Willie, her dying child. After the rehearsal the woman who was playing Mrs Carlyle beckoned me to come up on the stage. They gathered round and gave me sweets and asked me what I thought of the performance. I told them it was marvellous. Then they asked me would I like to be a real actress. Of course I told them I would. Then they told me they would give me a chance: would I like to play the part of little Willie?

I can laugh about it now, but then I was dead serious. I was given a little tutoring right on the spot.

I raced home to tell Mum. I talked fast, not giving her time to say anything. I just couldn't have borne it if she'd refused. Luckily for my theatrical ambitions Dad came home only once a fortnight. What a wonderful break it would be for us, I said. I dwelt on how many sovereigns I would get, and all the lovely things we would buy with the money.

As I watched Mum's face I knew that, although she was uncertain, she did not disapprove. In fact, I think she might have been a little pleased that her young daughter was about to make a stage début. When I could see that it was all right with her I implored her to come along with me and meet these wonderful people. But she wouldn't, as she really was a shy person. She just did not seem to like meeting people. Not like me! I loved meeting people.

It was arranged that Timothy would come with me, and after the show, Mum would be waiting outside somewhere in the shadows.

I was given a scrubbing until my body tingled and my hair shone. I was even allowed to wear my best dress, a little white muslin one that Mum made for me to wear to church. I'd never worn it because my mother had been waiting to get enough money to buy Timothy a new suit so that we could both go to church. By the time she had the money, our shoes had worn out and we had to wait until money had been saved to buy shoes. The vicious circle, so to speak, was never broken, so we never got around to going to church. Mother curled my hair round her finger and got a piece of blue ribbon from an old tin trunk that had Scotland printed on it in black lettering. She tied it around my waist. Timothy said I looked good and I felt good too.

I introduced Timothy to the cast and they allowed him to watch the performance from the wings.

We played to a packed house for four nights. Never once did I muff my single line!

I will never forget my stage mother as she leant over my death bed. She wept real tears that fell on my face and hair. She put all that she had into it. As she stroked my fair curls (which had been spread well out over my pillow just before the curtain went up) she cried: 'Willie! speak to me Willie! Willie! speak to me, for *I am your mother.*'

That was my cue. 'Mother!' I cried in a weak voice and, turning my head to one side, made a visible slump to indicate that I was dead. It brought the house down. The curtain kept opening and closing . . . people stamped and whistled.

It was the same on the last night. After what was to have been the last curtain, the clapping and stamping continued and the stage hand opened the curtain again just as I was about to scramble off my death bed in full view of the audience. Some laughed and others booed and whistled. The place was in an uproar. I remember deciding that they were upset because they thought I was really dead and seeing me sit up was a bit too much for them!

At the end of the show, the fat man who played the butler and who was the treasurer came over and paid me my salary for the four nights acting – two and sixpence! That was the biggest disappointment I'd had up to date. Tears smarted my eyes as I followed Timothy out to where Mum was waiting for us. She took the money without a word. I think she was as disappointed as I was.

4

The following week-end Dad came home. He was stone-cold sober and sullen. It seemed he didn't like batching; he missed my mother. He told her that the following fortnight we were to move to Glenbrook.

After he'd finished his meal he took his usual place on the hearth, hands thrust into pockets and back to the fire. Timothy and I exchanged furtive glances. We fully expected to get some sort of a dressing down, or perhaps an ear-bashing on what the 'Guver'ment' was doing to spoil the country. But much to our relief it soon became plain we were to be let off, for the time being at any rate, for he seemed to thaw a little and put himself out to be nice to Mum, as he began to tell her about his job and the plans he'd made for our camp life.

After a while he turned his attention to us, barking a command for us to hurry up and finish our dinner, and for me to 'look lively and git them dishes washed up'. I hastily gulped the remainder of my dinner. He ordered Timothy to 'shake it up and git the mornin' wood in'. Timothy slipped from his seat, clutching a piece of bread and disappeared to the wood heap.

Having brought the wood in, Timothy took up the tea-towel and began helping with the dishes. We hardly got started when he hinted to mother that it was time she went to bed. With a parting word to us to get to bed as soon as we finished the chores, he followed her to their room.

When we had finished in the kitchen I turned the lamp down low and it flickered out, leaving us in the dark. Then we quietly crept off to our room, and undressed by the light from the moon which glinted through the narrow little window by our bed. We were never allowed to take a light in case of fire. Rather silly seeing that father often threw the lighted lamp up against the wall when he came home drunk.

*

Soon the time came for us to move to Glenbrook. Father borrowed a horse and dray from someone at the camp, and Timothy helped him load our shabby bits of furniture and belongings on to it. Mother and I took the train to Glenbrook while Timothy rode on the dray with father.

I can remember every detail of that trip. Mother was dressed in a dark skirt and white cotton blouse. A white straw hat, with a wide black band was set squarely on the top of her head, and she carried an old battered suitcase. I carried a straw hamper the corners of which were broken away. It was almost as big as myself and bumped painfully against my little skinny legs as I carried it by the thin metal handgrip through which ran the leather straps.

The stationmaster at Glenbrook made some sort of joke to Mum about me carrying such a big hamper and gave me a sandwich from his tucker-tin which stood on the table in the booking office. There was no conveyance so we had to walk the two miles to the camp.

The camp site was called The Two Mile. It was fenced in with barbed wire to keep out straying cattle and had a large wire gate at the entrance. Most families had moved in when we arrived. Some had erected bark huts, others had merely pitched their tents. Much hammering was going on and dozens of kiddies played around while their mothers were seated on piles of bedding and belongings busily sewing corn bags which were to be used to line the inside of their dwellings.

The place was set out similar to Army camps, but with more space between each dwelling. Several boarding-houses built of canvas with iron roofs catered for the single men, who were camped well away from the married quarters. I found out later that all boarding-houses had bells and each one would wait until the other had finished ringing. Each bell having a different tone, the men knew which was their particular one.

A general store built of corrugated iron contained all kinds of goods, and right at the far end of the camp stood rows of water tanks filled regularly from water brought by train from a nearby reservoir.

As we walked along, Mum was trying to pick out which place belonged to us, when she saw an old towel, which she recognized as one she had given Dad. It was hanging over the door of one of the bark huts. She seemed a little uncertain as to whether we should go in or not, when a big jolly-looking man came over and asked: 'Were you looking for someone, Missus?' Mum said she was looking for our place, and told him our name. He said that she was right there at our place. He said he knew father very well and that we'd be neighbours. It turned out that it was his dray that father had borrowed to fetch our things. He hoped we'd get better acquainted, and invited us to visit his family as soon as we were settled in.

Mum thanked him nicely, but although we lived there for about two years she never became over-friendly with anyone, and certainly never visited anyone. But for all that everyone seemed to like and respect her.

She was seldom seen around and was never known to do any shopping – Timothy and I did that.

Our place consisted of two tents (our sleeping quarters) and a stringy-bark* hut which served as a kitchen and living room. The chimney was wide, built of stones and clay. In the yard near the chimney was a crude bench made out of saplings. On it stood a new tin dish, and beside it a cake of soap. It was obvious this was where Dad washed himself.

I followed Mum inside. The place was almost bare except for a box which Dad had been using for a table, and where he stored his food. In one of the tents where he'd been sleeping was a temporary bunk made of bags with sapling legs dug well into the earthen floor. Beside the bunk was another box; on it stood a candle in a pickle bottle. The candle was leaning to one side, where the grease had congealed around the bottle and on the box. A few old working togs, and heavy blucher boots lay in one corner.

Mum sat down on the edge of the bunk and looked despondently around the place. Looking back on it, I can guess what she was thinking, but she didn't say anything. Sensing that she wasn't too happy about it, I went over and sat close to her, not knowing what to say. As she raised a hand and drew the large hatpin from her hat I saw two tears roll off her cheeks. I couldn't understand why she should be unhappy about it, because to me it was a new adventure.

Later Dad and Timothy arrived with the furniture and belongings. Mum got busy and straightened things up, then cooked the dinner in a camp oven which was suspended from a piece of wire fastened to an iron bar fixed in the chimney.

Because father was getting better wages in his new job, we had better food. We were allowed to have butter and mother used to make gingerbread. Sometimes she would make an apple-pie. Yet we were by no means well fed. We rarely saw fruit as it was considered a luxury.

There were no recreation rooms in the camp, so everyone had to make their own pleasures. There wasn't an hotel for miles, but that didn't worry anyone, as someone had already started a sly-grog shop.

We saw little of Dad, for which we were thankful, as he would hurry over his evening meal, then take himself off to the sly-grog, or down the scrub at the back of the single men's quarters for a game of cards or two-up.† The men would sit

* A hut made of slabs of bark from the stringy-bark, one of the big eucalypts.

† Two-up. An Australian gambling game. Two pennies are tossed high in the air. The betting is on whether two heads or two tails will turn up.

around a big log fire in the open, telling blue jokes, and swearing like the devil.

Sometimes there would be a brawl, specially when someone dared to cheat at two-up. More than once a man was caught with two doubled-headed pennies. The penalty for this offence was usually a good kicking. The men always settled their own grievances.

Although it was a rough life, the people were, with rare exceptions, decent, hard-working folk. Of course there was loose conduct just as in any grouping of people.

There was Nellie, a wisp of a girl who was slushie at Mrs Murphy's boarding-house. Slushie was the name given to anyone who worked at a camp boarding-house. No one minded being called that.

She left the camp in a hurry and tongues began to wag. Mrs Murphy let it be known that Nellie had gone to Sydney to see a doctor as she had a growth. After some months Nellie came back, bringing the growth with her rolled in a woollen shawl. It was a lovely little boy. Of course, there were jokes made about Nellie's growth for weeks. But Nellie didn't seem to mind, she was quite proud of the little fellow. The sticky-beaks were dying to know who was the father of the baby, but Nellie wouldn't tell.

Mrs Murphy was rough and tough, but she stuck to Nellie, and because she had no kiddies of her own, she was good to them both, and treated the baby as though it belonged to her. Nellie used to put the baby in a fruit case outside the kitchen door so that she could keep an eye on him while working.

Then there was the Maltese who was caught eloping with another man's wife. The navvies made a hospital case of him.

There was big Pearly, whose husband left her. The single men used to chop wood and carry water for her. Incidentally her wood pile was the envy of all the other women in the camp. Soon it became apparent that they had not always confined their efforts to these tasks, for some of them became sick, and had to go to Sydney. I remember at the time I puzzled my brain trying to work out how any woman could make a man sick, but no one enlightened me. In the end, some of the men who had growing sons, got to work and drove her out of the camp.

There was Paddy, a bald-headed Irishman who kept the general store. He used to take advantage of the Maltese who could not speak English. I often saw him charge a shilling a lb.

for sugar (then 1½d. a lb.), and overcharge jam, rice and other items. He used to follow the camps as they moved along, and eventually made his fortune.

Timothy and I soon chummed up with the Medley family. Joshua the father we had met the first day. His wife's name was Emmy. His son Chris was about Timothy's age. He was boisterous and happy-go-lucky like his father. The daughter Esther was a nice girl with blue-black hair which she wore in pigtails. She had lovely brown eyes and a creamy skin. She was easy to get along with as she was quiet and reserved.

The Medley family had migrated from England a few years before, but because work wasn't too plentiful they had decided to try camp life for a while. Joshua Medley had had a dispute with his father in England and when he came out to Australia he decided to forget his relatives in the 'Old Dart',* so he changed his name by deed-poll. Esther told me that when they went to the Registrar General's department they were trying to decide among themselves what their new name would be, and just as they were about to enter the building a band in the park started playing a medley of waltzes. So Joshua decided the name would be Medley.

There must have been something behind the rift between Joshua and his father for him to change his name. He was a most likeable man who got along with everyone. He was immensely popular among the men and he certainly was popular with us. He was kind to Timothy and me and let us visit their place quite a lot. Probably he knew that Dad wasn't so good as a father. Mr Medley was nice to his own children, in fact they were good pals. Esther and Chris could ask him things and he'd answer them nicely. Sometimes he and Chris would put on the gloves and spar, and Esther was allowed to play the piano. How I envied them their home life.

Joshua went to great pains to make their camp home nice. He papered the walls, and even put boarded floors down and Mrs Medley bought cheap rugs and spread them out and made pretty curtains for the tiny windows. They were the only people in the camp to own a piano. That was the closest I had been to a real piano and believe me I thought it was the most wonderful thing in the world. The piano, by the way, was one that Joshua had picked up at a second-hand shop in Sydney and looked the worse for wear and the keys had turned yellow. It needed a good tuning too, but I didn't

* Slang term for England.

20

notice anything wrong with it then. I had only one thought, if only I could play!

Joshua Medley once saw me watching Esther with what I suppose was a rapt expression on my face and told her to let me have a go on the piano for a while. Needless to say I was thrilled and sat down while Esther began showing me how to do the five-finger exercise. The discord I created was terrific, but no one seemed to mind the din. Joshua sat near the fire mending the family's shoes and his wife sat opposite him knitting. After that night I haunted the Medley home. In a few months I had learnt to play little pieces by ear.

5

The two Medley kids and Timothy and I became good mates. We even made a pact to stick together for ever. We had a sort of ceremony to make it binding. This was carried out under the Knapsack bridge one Saturday afternoon. Timothy seemed a bit sweet on Esther right from the beginning. He would always stay close to her and would carry her books to and from school. As far as I can remember sex matters, the mysteries of babies, etc., were never discussed amongst us kids. However, someone in the camp owned a bright pink flannelette nightgown and it was the custom for it to be loaned to anyone expecting a baby; so when we happened to see it hanging on a line, we would whisper to each other about Mrs So-and-so must be getting a little baby soon. Sure enough we were right.

Timothy and I had to do all the chores, like carting water and keeping up the wood supply. We carried the water in two pails suspended from a yoke, in the fashion of the Chinese market-gardener with his baskets. Besides this, I used to mind Nellie's baby at mealtimes for an hour or so, until Nellie had got through waiting on table. They had a cow bell which Nellie would bring outside and ring to warn the men their meals were ready. But Dad didn't consider this was enough for me and when I was twelve he told mother it was time I got out and did a bit of work! He had come home fighting drunk – Albert's grog was not only hard on the purse but on the head and the stomach. Dad chucked things round, and roared that he was tired of sweating his guts out for us and reminded us how lucky we were. That he'd had to work all his life, and that the first pair of boots he ever wore he'd bought from the money he earned selling papers on the Quay.

He'd already got Timothy a job on the railroad as a nipper. A nipper was the name given to a young boy whose job it was to boil the billies and carry the various tools, such as picks and shovels, to the men when required. The first day some of the men got hold of Timothy and forcibly removed his pants to make sure (as they said) he was not a girl. This was a sort of initiation to the job.

Before long Dad had me installed at Mrs Hussler's boarding-house. I had to go there for an hour in the morning and after school. For this I was paid two and sixpence a week. Mrs Hussler was a tyrant to say the least. I had to work like a slave. I worked week-ends too.

Besides being a slave-driver she had a passion for hoarding things and often took the train to Penrith on Saturdays to attend auction sales. One Saturday morning she was going to take me along with her to help carry her parcels, but I was already up to my eyes in the kitchen and couldn't be spared. However, she got a youngster in the camp to go in my place.

When she came to pay me my wages that night she only gave me two shillings explaining that, as I couldn't get through my work in time to go with her, she'd obliged to get someone else to go. Therefore, she had to pay him out of my money.

When Dad was told he found me another job where my wages wouldn't be interfered with.

*

When I reached a certain stage in my life, mother told me one or two things concerning the facts of life; but not very much. Then Dad built a bark hut for Timothy, leaving me with the tent to myself.

It seemed now that I was growing up. I no longer wanted to go bird's-nesting with Timothy, or ride horses bare-back.

I made a patchwork rug for my bedside and trimmed my dressing-table, which was only a deal wood case, with some old curtains which I'd salvaged from someone's rubbish heap. I bought a small mirror from Paddy's shop and propped it up on the table. I got to looking at myself in the mirror and would put my hair up on top just to see what I looked like.

I started making my own clothes, but this proved difficult

as Dad wouldn't allow me to use the machine. No reason, sheer nastiness.

Was there *anything* good about him? Well, once, when I was ill, he brought my bunk inside before the fire and sat by me several nights. He gave me drinks, and made me comfortable, but hardly spoke. Every now and then he would stoke the fire then return to his seat at the fire. No little words of comfort to his sick kid. He was hard as nails. He stayed with me until morning on each of these nights, then mother took over and he would go off to work.

Whenever I was in trouble with other kids, he stuck up for me in front of them, but when we were alone he'd give me hell, even if I was in the right.

*

I used to dream of the time when I would be able to get away from this sort of life. I began to turn my thoughts to Sydney. I'd get there somehow. I wanted to live in a proper house, wear nice clothes, get a nice job and some day I'd get married and have children of my own. I'd see they had a better life than I had. It was a dreary kind of existence. If there had been no trees to climb or horses around, I don't know what I would have done for amusement.

An old woman who acted as midwife at the camp began calling on mother. She came several times, which could only mean one thing: Mum was going to have another baby.

One week-end Mum and I had the place to ourselves, as Dad and Timothy had gone to Mulgoa to break some horses for a farmer. All day Saturday I never let up on the sewing machine and on Sunday Mum allowed me to make cakes and toffee. I had a wonderful time. But Mum didn't seem too well and spent most of the time lying around. She talked to me a lot, mostly about her girlhood days in Scotland and about her grandparents who were extremely good to her. I don't think she liked her life in Australia. Late that night she came to my tent and woke me. She was standing there holding a candle, its grease dripping on her hand. I could see at once she was ill. Her face was grey and drawn. On the front of her white flannelette nightgown was a crimson stain. Her teeth chattered as she told me to get up quickly and go and fetch Liza, the midwife. I darted out of the tent pulling my dress on over my head as I went. Eliza said something about expecting me. I noticed she was fully dressed and was sitting dozing by the fire. We returned together and she promptly started giving me orders. Light the fire! She must have boiling water, plenty of it. Get this! Do that!

When I'd filled every pot and put them on the fire I went over to the table and began looking at some tiny garments that Mum must have put there in readiness for the coming event. They were baby clothes and a pair of new white Turkish towels. I remembered these were on the grocery list a few months back. Paddy had sent a special order for them to Sydney because he only had rough coloured ones in stock. There was also a brand new white enamel wash basin. It, too, had been a special order. A cake of Pears unscented baby soap stood beside the dish.

Soon the water was boiling and Eliza came out and rolling up her sleeves she began to scrub her hands and arms. She was only about two jam tins high, and just as round. She puffed as she leant over the dish.

She was a bossy little person and expected me to run the minute she gave an order. Soon after she went in to Mum I heard the faint cry of a new-born baby. Then I heard Eliza smacking the baby to make it cry properly. There was a pause, while I waited, my ears cocked for another sound from my baby sister or brother, but none came.

Shortly afterwards Eliza emerged. She looked very serious: 'Get over to Medley's and tell Mr Medley to go and get Dr Rigard. And don't waste a second.'

Once out of sight I hesitated for a moment, then decided to go for the doctor myself. I had enough sense to know that something must be seriously wrong for Eliza to call a doctor, for in most confinements in those days a midwife did the job herself.

I didn't wake Mr Medley, but raced over to where Paddy kept his stable. It was made of iron bark, with a rough sapling fence. In it were two horses, Foley, an old cart horse, and Scarlet, a blood-mare chestnut with white socks. She didn't get her name because of her colour, but for her temper. Paddy had brought her from a travelling circus. Father had broken her, but only just! Just after he had broken her he made me ride her. She tossed me off and he made me get back on straight away, so as not to lose my nerve. But I was always a bit scared of her after that.

Without asking Paddy's permission I crept into the feed house and took his saddle from the wall. I then sidled alongside Scarlet and, trembling with cold and fear, patted her gently, calling her softly by name. She began to prance, shaking her head as she wheeled around and around as I struggled with the saddle and drew in the girths, making them doubly tight. I sprang up into the saddle, but realized too late that I'd forgotten to let the slip rails down. Scarlet didn't let a little thing like that worry her – she took the rails in her stride, clearing the fence like a steeplechaser, on the first lap of the ride to the next camp five miles away.

Scarlet bent to the bridle and munched savagely on the bit as we hit the main road. I took a firm grip on the reins, but her mouth was so powerful, I had to give her her head. She just about bolted with me.

It was bitterly cold and a strong westerly was blowing which cut into my body and blew my hair criss-cross about my face. My bare feet were half frozen in the stirrups and my dress was somewhere up around my thighs. We came to a level-crossing; the gates were closed because of a coming goods train. Scarlet pulled up abruptly, nearly sending me over her head. She pranced impatiently around and around like a circus horse, and when the train had passed and the gates were opened we were off again. I managed to stick on somehow till I got to the doctor's. Although it was cold, the mare was sweating and showing foam about her shoulders.

Dr Rigard, the Government Medical Officer, was housed in a long wooden house similar to a railway carriage; it was on wheels, so that when the camp moved along the mountain all the doctor had to do was to sit in his house and allow himself to be towed. He was sitting in his study reading. When I gasped out my story he got out his roan and we started back home.

I shall never forget that ride. Scarlet took it a bit easier going back. She seemed to like keeping company with the roan, which was very fast too. I was sick with fear of what might be happening. A storm was coming up. Lightning flashed, and black and white clouds scudded across the sky. We just made it before the rain came.

When we arrived back at the camp the Medleys, Joshua and his wife, were outside our tent. The doctor bustled to Mum's bedside, where Eliza was waiting. Then father and Timothy arrived. Soon the doctor came out and spoke quietly to father while Timothy and I stayed close together. The doctor rode away. There was nothing he could do for Mum, she was too far gone by the time he reached her. The baby was dead and Mum died a few minutes after we arrived.

6

If our home had been unhappy while my mother was alive, it was hell after she died. Looking back on it now I think that Dad must really have cared for her in his own peculiar way. Probably much of his bad behaviour came from his sense of inferiority. If he had been jealous of Timothy and me before, now he seemed positively to hate us. The job of housekeeping fell on me and it was a hard job for a fifteen-year-old girl. Cooking in a primitive camp oven, washing and mending the filthy working clothes for two men, cleaning the hut and the tents – always up before sunrise in the attempt to get everything spick and span and keep my father sweet.

I missed my mother desperately and Timothy, I think, missed her even more. He had always been her favourite. Dad spent most of the time at the grog shop or the two-up ring, coming home only to eat and sleep and to rage at us for a useless pair of brats who, in some unspecified way I could never make out, were responsible for my mother's death.

Yes, that camp was hell for us, and we lived for the day we could get away from it. I used to read the scraps of newspaper that came round the meat and the other food parcels, studying all the advertisements and the pictures about Sydney. I used to borrow the Medleys' newspaper and pore over it. One day I swore when I was old enough to make the break I'd go to Sydney. Esther and I dreamed of Sydney.

Release came for Timothy in a way we'd never dreamed of. The war broke out and Timothy, who was tall for his age, passed himself off as being older than he was and enlisted. Father raved and threatened to put his pot on to the Military. But he never did. It was as though with Mum's death a spring had snapped in him.

Timothy went overseas. I cried the day I watched his train go out. He was all that I had. He was killed in the landing on Gallipoli. Even today I can't think of that without a sense of the stupidity and wastefulness of life. Esther Medley wept with me when the news came and I realized that there was a lot more to the boy-and-girl friendship than I'd ever guessed. Suddenly she seemed much older than I was. She grew thin and pale and couldn't settle to anything and without any warning she made up her mind to go to Sydney and get a job.

I was unhappier than ever when Esther left. She wrote me glowing letters from the city which, though it was only thirty miles away, seemed to me to be on another planet. Dad threatened what he wouldn't do to me if I even so much as thought of following Esther. He'd put the law on to me, he would!

I went on cooking and washing and cleaning up, saving a penny here and a penny there towards my fare and some clothes, helping at one of the boarding-houses when Dad was safely out of the way. Always with only one thought in my mind.

Then Esther wrote to say she could get me a job where she was working and I could share her room. Dad was away on a job farther up the mountains. I put my few clothes into the battered hamper, took the thirty-seven shillings I had managed to save from the baking-powder tin I had buried under the bunk in my tent, walked into Glenbrook and took a train to Sydney.

7

I must have looked a regular bushwhacker* the day I stepped out of the train on to Central Station. What a fright! Home-made skirt and blouse, mended cotton gloves that had belonged to mother. And what to me was the crowning glory – a red satin hat (also homemade) trimmed with brown fur. I was shivering with excitement as Esther – looking to me like something out of a fashion-plate, made her way along the crowded platform. She took me straight out to her room and next day I began work.

My job was serving behind the counter at Hillier's in Pitt Street, then the most up-to-date and fashionable café of its kind in Sydney. It sold, in addition to delicious concoctions such as pêche Melba and banana splits, excellent chocolates and

* Bushwhacker—person who lives in the bush well away from big towns or cities.

candies. And that was Esther's and my job. The shop seemed a fairyland to me: glittering lights, glass counters, waitresses in attractive uniforms, and a ceaseless flow of customers who seemed to me the embodiment of all the people I'd read of in fashion magazines.

My lack of clothes didn't matter, for at the shop we wore a smart uniform and at home I was soon busy making myself a wardrobe from remnants I picked up at sales and with the aid of complicated paper patterns which I used to spread out on the floor, as we had no table large enough in our room. Esther had a good dress sense but she couldn't sew, so under her direction I sewed for both of us. I learned from the shop window displays, the various ladies' journals and our customers, what to wear and how to wear it.

I forgot my loneliness. I forgot my father. I was in a dazzle of constant excitement. Evidently I blossomed out in unexpected ways for men customers began passing compliments to me as I sold them sweets. At first I was surprised, taking it for granted that Esther, with her film star good looks should attract all the attention. Then I was delighted. It gave me a new confidence in myself. After the first six months I got a rise.

But by then something much more exciting had happened. It seemed that all the dreams I had dreamed in the slab hut at Glenbrook were being realized. I met John Marsh.

He was quite the most handsome man I'd ever met and certainly the best dressed. Long before he spoke to me I used to watch him as he went each day to the seat he always occupied for lunch. Even before I knew him he was my ideal – tall and fair with closely-cropped hair that crinkled and grew well down over his temples where it would flash like gold where the light caught it.

When he first began to linger at the counter I thought he was attracted by Esther. She told him about Timothy's death and he was very sympathetic. He explained rather vaguely that he'd have liked to join up himself, but there were reasons why he had to stay home.

He charmed both Esther and me with his ready wit and the lovely way he spoke. After all, we were just two country kids. He seemed to have a lot of knowledge of things and could talk with ease. Naturally Esther and I were thrilled. We'd never met anyone like him in our lives.

Then he suggested that we might both like to join the

Tennis Club to which he belonged. The way we scrimped and saved to buy those tennis rackets! And the nights I sat up making our tennis frocks by hand – from the latest patterns! Of course our game was terrible but the sociability of the club was a joy to us both. And I think the most exciting and surprising moment of my life occurred when, a few weeks later, John Marsh invited me to go to the club dance with him.

Esther was very surprised when I told her I was going with John. Somehow she had taken it as much for granted as I had that I should be content with her disappointed swains who liked to confide in me. And here was quite the most presentable young man at the club picking *me* out!

I slaved over those evening dresses – the first I'd ever had. Esther looked a picture in a maize-coloured taffeta. I don't know exactly how I looked in a frock made of soft cream lace I had picked up at a bargain sale, with a bunch of pink roses at my waist. But when John called for me and told me I was as pretty as a picture I walked on air. Cinderella couldn't have been more overwhelmed by the Prince's attention.

I tried to make myself worthy of him. I had rather vague ideas of what worthy actually meant, but I remember I became careful in my speech and manners to the point almost of primness. I read all the books John spoke about.

By tacit consent Esther and I never spoke about the camp. We tried to forget all about it. I, for one, almost succeeded. Even when I got the news that Dad had been killed in a railway accident, it seemed something out of another life! I couldn't honestly pretend to grieve for him. And when one evening about six months after we had met, John asked me to marry him, I really believed I was the happiest girl in the world. The following Sunday he took me out to meet his mother.

I made sure to look my best that afternoon. I was dressed in a cream suit, a bunch of violets in my lapel. I felt fine. I was too short to measure up the standards of Esther's classic beauty, but I had a tiny waist, good teeth and skin. There were two or three freckles on my nose. John teased me about them, and laughed at my nose because it was too little. My hair was wavy but of a rather nondescript brown. How I longed to have Esther's glossy black plaits or the curly corn-coloured mop of the other girl at our counter. I tried to make the best of myself – not so much from vanity as from the wish to justify John's choice. I needn't have wasted my time!

It was a brilliant winter afternoon when John led me down the street where he lived in one of the best parts of Stanmore. It was wide and well kept. His home wasn't a mansion when one saw the other houses there, but it was large enough to impress me, austere on the outside, with marble steps leading up to the front door. The hall was like a room it was so wide, beautifully covered with thick carpet. It certainly wasn't austere indoors. He took me into the drawing-room. I'd never been in such a lovely room before, its rich furnishings and softly shaded windows made it seem restful as well as beautiful. To my inexperienced eyes it was all wonderful.

The Mater, as he called her, was sitting in a high-backed chair surrounded by satin cushions. When John introduced us I went forward to shake hands with her, a little too quickly in my anxiety to meet her. She repulsed me in a quiet way and only proffered the tips of her fingers in a limp handshake. My first rebuff. But I soon forgot that, feeling secure in the knowledge that I would make her like me. I'd be so good to her, etc.

My mother-in-law-to-be was short and plump with tiny feet and hands and lovely fair skin without a blemish. Her hair was blonde, the golden colour of peroxide blonde but it was her natural colouring. She wore her hair in a sort of Pompadour, which somehow suited her pompous manner. She had lovely arms and knew it and took great care of them. They, too, were without blemish and so shapely and dimpled. Her hands were white and soft, but too small and a little too plump for beauty and were always loaded with rings with beautiful settings. Her eyes were small and sky blue. She had once been very pretty, perhaps even beautiful. She was so fair that her friends had dubbed her Snow. She always dressed in things that suited her. That day she was wearing some sort of a silk gown in a soft shade of blue that brought out the colour of her eyes.

While we were taking stock of each other, a young friend of John's called. He was a nice boy and dressed in cream flannels and carried a tennis racket. John introduced us, then went off with his friend to a game of tennis on their own court at the back of the house. He said something about leaving us two women to get better acquainted. Only one game he promised and he'd be back. So I was left to face her. She took in everything about me. I was fully conscious of that. She asked me about my family and my education and I did my best to present things in their best light without lying but I don't think she was impressed.

She touched a little silver bell on the table at her elbow. This brought Martha Tuppa into the room. She was dressed in a black silk dress done up to the neck. I found later she always dressed like this on Sunday afternoons. John's mother asked her to bring in the afternoon tea. She disappeared to return wheeling a mobile tray. It was laden with scones and cakes. I was feeling hungry, but had enough sense to take only one morsel from the plate which Martha handed to me.

The Mater poured the tea, three cups, one for Martha. Martha sat down with us. She had certain privileges, because she was a lady's help. Many a time she would remind me she was not a servant, but a lady's help. Yet she did all the menial tasks. In fact, she did everything that had to be done in that house. She sat there and listened to our conversation. I know now that, from that very first meeting, she put me in her class and kept me there to the last. It was obvious that she took sides with the Mater against me. Because she was a slave to this woman, cringing and crawling, she expected me to be the same.

I never made any progress either with the Mater or Martha. My mother-in-law was a pannikin* snob as my father would have said. She hadn't enough money to go into Sydney Society, though she used to boast that her ancestors had come out as free settlers in the early days and that she was entitled to mix with the Pure Merinos.† As she had to be content with her own small set in this then-affulent suburb, apparently the other Pure Merinos wanted a big bank balance as well as a name.

8

We were married just at the end of World War One when I was eighteen and John was twenty-five. It was a very quiet affair, my mother-in-law's excuse being that as my father had recently died it wouldn't be nice to have a fuss. I knew even

* From pannikin boss – a person of very minor authority.

† 'Pure Merino' – satirical term used to describe the descendants of the early Free Settlers who thought themselves superior to Emancipists.

then that her real reason was that she was ashamed that John wasn't making a better match.

Because I had no background, as she termed it, my mother-in-law never forgave me. However she provided us with a nice home next door to her and the adjoining fence was fitted with a strategically-placed gate through which she would come, rather like a latter-day Queen Victoria, to rule our home as rigidly as she did her own.

She was hard and selfish; but she had one weakness – John, whom she had spoilt from babyhood by giving in to him and never alllowing him to stand on his own feet. In her eyes and Martha's, John could do no wrong.

When I married John Marsh, I had no doubt that we were going to live happily ever after. To begin with I was madly in love with him and accepted quite uncritically everything he did. Also, for the first time in my life I had a real home and I tried to make it as attractive and happy as I could.

We lived a gay enough life that first year. Tennis on the court behind my mother-in-law's house, dances and theatres. John loved the theatre, seldom missing a good show. I remember he took me five times to see 'Chu Chin Chow'. Always in the best seats, of course.

When he lost the job he had when we first married I was indignant at his unsympathetic boss and I begged him to cut down our expenditure, but he just laughed. There were plenty more jobs and plenty more money. As though to prove it he received a legacy from someone. It amounted to about eight hundred pounds. That was a fair sum in those days, but it did not take long to spend it.

He was highly amused when I pleaded with him to buy a small business. He wanted to know what I would do in a business. It was always like that. No one could tell him anything. So I had to sit back and see the money go for nothing. It worried me, but I thought 'John knows best,' just as I agreed with him when he explained that it was for the best that he'd left his second job so soon. I firmly believed that some day he would find the job that suited him and that everything would be all right.

When within sixteen months Terry was born there seemed nothing more in the world I could wish for.

I had seen Terry's birth as the last thing needed to make our marriage perfect and it took quite a while for it to dawn on me that John didn't see it that way. While he seemed fond enough of his baby son he wasted no time on him and obviously resented our social activities being limited by his arrival. He began spending a lot of time at his club. He was a member of one of the best sporting clubs in town which meant a rate of spending he could not have afforded had it not been for the fat cheques handed out to him by his mother from time to time.

I soon wakened to the fact that it was his mother who kept up the supply of jobs for him. These she obtained through her many influential friends. When one of his jobs would fall through she would sort out the people he had already worked for and go to work on others. So it would happen that John would get another job – cushy and not too strenuous.

But to John no job was cushy enough and soon he would be out of employment once again. Between jobs it was his mother who attended to our household accounts. Naturally this was very humiliating to me.

When I tried to talk about this with her she turned on me in fury and said everything was my fault. If I'd given John a really happy home he would have settled down long ago.

From the time I mentioned the household accounts she started a campaign of persecution, so subtle that I couldn't actually find anything to complain about to John.

Her offsider in this was Martha Tuppa, the maid who had been in the Marsh service for more than thirty years. Martha was tall and angular. Her long narrow face was like old leather, and her eyes, which were small and dark, gave the impression of always being half closed; remarkable indeed, for she never missed a thing. She could neither read nor write, but to make up for these shortcomings she possessed a remarkable memory and kept a mental record of all dates and matters of importance to the family.

If Martha happened to be washing the dishes and the phone rang the clatter of crockery would cease, only to be renewed with energy when the conversation had ended.

She was orphaned when quite young and the Marshes had taken her into their home. But as soon as she was able to wield a broom she became the household drudge. The tragedy of her young life had left its imprint: she disliked all young people and hated all men. She showed no sympathy towards me and took her cue from her mistress in her attitude. They both worshipped Terry as they worshipped John, and I had to be firm to prevent him from being completely spoilt.

33

Sometimes Esther would drop in for dinner and we would spend the rest of the evening together while John went off to his club. She still lived in a room and batched for herself and I used to make her simple little frocks in an effort to help her balance her budget from her meagre wages.

John didn't resent her coming, although he had done his best when we were first married to discourage any other friends I had. He'd never been a stay-at-home and now I had a second baby coming, he began going out much more at night, sometimes arriving home well after midnight. He moved into the spare room saying he was so often late getting home that he didn't want to disturb me.

One evening I decided to have a serious talk with him. I made up my mind to be tactful at all costs, in the hope that we might be able to sort things out. Esther came to dinner, upsetting my plans. If Esther noticed anything was wrong between John and me she hid the fact and made no comment, something I appreciated in her for I couldn't have borne any real criticism of John from anyone.

On this particular evening, when John had gone I mentioned to Esther that a dress I had been making was ready for a fitting. However, she seemed in a hurry to leave, murmuring something about having an appointment and that she must not be late. Glancing at her wrist watch she said rather anxiously: 'I've only a few minutes, will it take long?'

'No, I won't be a jiffy, I just want to take your length.'

She hurried out of her dress and flung it on a chair and I helped her into the new one. As she stood erect waiting for me to pin the hem of her frock I noticed her restless look.

I was glad she couldn't see my face as I knelt on the floor; I felt a certain disloyalty in discussing John even with Esther.

'I'm very worried about John,' I said. 'He seems to have changed towards me in the last few months.'

She gave a start. Thinking that I'd stuck a pin in her, I said 'Oh, I'm sorry Esther.'

She stammered, 'No, it – it's all right. What were you saying?'

I repeated what I'd said, but she merely replied, 'Haven't you any idea what could be wrong?' and quickly changed the subject by drawing my attention back to the frock.

As I helped her out of the dress she pulled her arms free, and glancing at her wrist watch, exclaimed: 'Heavens, I simply must fly.'

I offered to walk to the tramstop with her, but she refused, saying that she would be much quicker if she went by herself.

I was feeling miserable enough, but said flippantly: 'Why, who's the lucky man, Esther?'

I fancied she coloured as she retorted, 'Don't be silly.'

I made no answer as I kissed her, then watched her as she went down the steps and along the garden path.

From then onward Esther's visits fell off and I felt lonelier than ever.

I returned indoors to find Terry had gone to sleep and the house was quiet except for the grandfather clock ticking in the hall.

I decided to stay awake until John came home and have the little chat I had planned earlier, but I didn't see him again that night as I dozed off after hearing the clock strike twelve.

Entirely unsuspecting, thinking that most of our troubles were caused by the nearness of my mother-in-law, I made a quick decision. Next morning I took the children with me and went house-hunting and found a small cottage in an industrial area. Paying the agent a week's rent I collected the keys and returned home. I thought that John, seeing my determination and being confronted with the new latch-key, would fall in with my plans, but I was mistaken. He was furious with me, and said, 'You can get out, but you can leave Terry here.'

I exclaimed, 'Don't be silly, John!'

'I'm not silly,' he snapped. 'The Mater can look after him.'

I didn't think he meant what he said, but I knew that his mother coveted the child.

I returned the keys of the cottage to the agent next day and made up my mind to make the most of my life in our present home.

I'd thought that if John had been agreeable to move away from his mother and be content for us to manage on his wage, we might make something of our lives together. But I didn't take a trick. The odds were against me. John had no intention of breaking with his mother who represented security and comfort to him.

9

When Ann was born I thought things would readjust themselves. I didn't see how any man could resist such an enchanting wee thing as Ann. But things didn't readjust themselves. John continued to occupy the spare bedroom, saying he couldn't afford to have his night's rest broken by a squalling baby when he had to work hard all day.

He lost his job again and I said what I thought about his idea of hard work. He was furious and we had our first real quarrel – the first of many.

We began to quarrel mildly at first, then furiously, saying unkind things to each other. I was horrified. I simply didn't know what was happening to us. It seemed, too, that John welcomed these quarrels, as he became irritable and aggressive on the slightest provocation. I couldn't do anything right.

It was during one of John's periodic spells between jobs that I conceived the idea of getting something to do – some sort of job that would bring me in a little pocket money; for I was already tired of depending on my mother-in-law for every little thing. I felt that I'd like to get some money off my own bat. I hadn't to look far, for there it was on the back page of the *Herald* – 'Wanted a wet nurse – good money paid right person to save a baby's life.'

The thought of saving a life appealed to me. I sprang into action. After phoning to make an appointment I dressed myself and Ann and caught a tram to Central, where I picked up another which took us to Centennial Park.

The house I was looking for was a large brick mansion which stood well back from the road. Its well kept lawns sloped towards the street. Earlier applicants were seated on the wide verandah. Several glass doors led on to this verandah. One of them stood open, it was the library.

The women were chattering away, each certain she'd get the job. One large woman, dressed in black and without corsets and brassiere, assured us that she'd be a cert to get the job, seeing that she had so much milk it was often necessary for her to lean over the bath to let it run away. However, I knew from my conversation on the phone that the doctor in the case would be more interested in the quality of the milk.

As if to give emphasis to what she'd said she drew everyone's attention to her blouse where the dampness was beginning to show in widening round spots.

A little woman sitting close to me seemed the most unlikely. She was thin and pale, and her scraggy hair was shedding dandruff on to the collar of her black coat which looked as old as she was herself. She looked as though she needed medical attention. A nursing sister came to the door and called my name. I rose and she beckoned me. As I passed through the door I heard a resentful murmur. I imagined them saying: 'Why should she be the first in seeing that she was the last to arrive.' They were not to know, of course, that I had phoned for the appointment.

The doctor, a Macquarie Street specialist, tall and distinguished looking, was seated at a desk. A woman sat next to the doctor. I knew at once that she was mother of the baby whose life I wanted to save. She was about my age, I thought, and beautiful.

The only way I could describe her was that she seemed all sort of golden – her hair, her dress and everything about her gave me that impression. Here, I thought, was a woman who had everything – but milk for her baby!

I took a firm grip on Ann, hoping she wouldn't be restless in this company. The doctor asked me a lot of questions – how was my general health? – had I ever had a serious illness and so on. I told him my health was good and that I had never been seriously ill in my life. I was asked if I would agree to a blood test which the doctor explained was the usual procedure. I agreed at once.

The doctor and the nurse then left the room for a few minutes, leaving me alone with the lovely lady. She told me that if the blood test was satisfactory I would get the job. Then we got down to tin-tacks – the money. How much did I want? I hadn't thought how much, as I had left that to her. She was prepared to pay good money, that was what the ad stated. When I hesitated she said: 'I thought of paying you two guineas a week.'

By now I had taken in the scene – everything spoke of great wealth. I said I'd take the job for three guineas. She thought for a while and agreed. I was given the drill, I was to live in, etc. She then left me.

The nursing sister returned with the under-nurse who took Ann from me and disappeared with her crying lustily. The doctor came in and gave me a thorough examination, took blood from my arm, with the sister standing by giving and taking the instruments. When it was time for me to leave, the sister pressed a button on the desk, and the under-nurse returned with Ann, who by now was quite happy.

The sister picked up a pencil and pad as she walked with me to the door. She told me that, if the test was in order, a car would come for me late next afternoon. I would be notified in either case.

As I left, she began taking addresses from the other applicants. I felt a cool breeze as I passed out, and did not look back. I felt sure that the job was mine – and began to feel a bit worried. What would John have to say to all this? Surely he wouldn't object seeing it was for a good cause. And the doctor had assured me that Ann would not suffer from the experience. The baby did not have an infectious disease, he was just starving and needed building up. His mother had weaned him too soon and then the trouble had started.

John didn't seem to mind. Martha agreed to look after him and Terry. I really think they were all glad to be rid of me for a while.

Late next afternoon a large car rolled to a stop at my front gate. I watched from the window and saw a chauffeur get out and make his way up the garden path. I ran and opened the door before he had time to touch the bell. He handed me a letter written in a good hand, then moved away turning his back as I opened it. I was to have the job – the chauffeur had instructions to wait and take me there.

It did not take me long as I was already prepared. Ann and I went off in the car. A trim maid showed me to my room, a guest room, and one of the best in the house – that is, if there were any best rooms, as they were all very grand. The chauffeur brought my luggage into my room.

I was given the freedom of the house. Not that I took advantage of it, but I did, now and again, have a look at the lovely drawing-room which fascinated me. It was decorated in cream with a scarlet carpet – a cream baby-grand, etc. At five o'clock I was to give baby Carl (for that was the name of the heir) his feed.

The sister, who proved to be a very nice person, led me to a room on the first floor . . . it was the last word in nurseries.

The under-nurse came and took Ann from my arms.

The sister prepared me for the baby's feed. I sat on a low stool while she bathed my breasts with some solution, placed a gown about me, one of those white things that doctors wear at the operating table. Then she left me to return almost immediately with my new foster child. He was a dear little fellow – like his mother in colouring, but oh so thin and weak. My heart went out to him at once. I put him to my breast, but he did not make much of an effort. I was persevering with him when the door opened and his mother entered, dressed in evening dress and bringing with her the faint perfume of roses. She looked on for a while, and when it seemed that the child did not want to make any real effort, she began putting on an act there and then, blamed me, it must be my fault. Naturally I became upset, the baby more upset and the sister at last removed him from my knee.

Afterwards the nurse told me in confidence that the woman was completely neurotic, which explained her stupid behaviour.

I did not see Carl again that night, but was told that I would have to be up at six in the morning. It appeared that the doctor had prescribed for me. I was to be driven in the park every morning at six-thirty, something about fresh air being good for the mother's milk. The chauffeur was to drive me. I was allowed to take Ann along with me.

You can imagine me sitting up kidding I was a lady. The big car was not used on these jaunts, merely a Packard! with the hood down to let the sun and air in.

I had my meals with the family. But the mother never came down to breakfast. The head of the house went to his office every day. He was in the shipping business. She was a pampered pet of rich parents and richer in-laws. She put on several acts like that of the first day. She accused me of being pregnant; something must be wrong; always my fault.

At last, when I felt that Carl wasn't getting very far with me, I told her I'd go. The husband pleaded with me; said if I'd stay he'd help my husband into a good job. He begged me to reconsider, but I just didn't want to put up with her. Besides, by this time John was beginning to moan about me being absent from the home. Pure cantankerousness, because his behaviour when I returned was more casual and rude then ever. In any case I knew by now that no one could help John keep a job.

I had thought when I took the job that it might do John good to miss me for a while, but when I came back I realized that all that had happened was that he had been been completely spoiled by his mother's and Martha's attentions. Terry, who was three, came in for a lot of spoiling, too, as he was a great favourite with them both, mainly, I think, because he strongly resembled his father.

Long before Terry was three he had the situation well in hand, and knew, in the way that children have of knowing these things, that he could handle his grandmother quite easily. With Ann it was quite different. I think it would have been almost impossible to spoil her; she was a lovely child with a sweet disposition. At a year old she resembled her father except that her hair was like mine, dark brown, soft and curly.

10

Things got steadily worse instead of better: John persisted in sleeping in the spare room and he went out more than ever at night. He began to pick quarrels on the slightest provocation and sometimes with no provocation at all. I grew to dread the week-ends when he was home all the time. Even worse were the weeks between jobs, for by now he couldn't hold a job for more than a few weeks. There were endless scenes and I began to grow so nervy and worried that I was nearly as touchy as he.

During these scenes Martha Tuppa generally found some excuse for coming into our house. When John told her to get to hell, she'd listen at the key hole. He caught her more than once. Of course she relayed everything to my mother-in-law.

During these times ,my only confidante was Esther. She had the freedom of my home as I always felt sorry for her because she hadn't much of a life. When John booked seats for a show (which was often), because of the children I often offered to let Esther go in my place.

When I came to think of it later, she always seemed to be conveniently around, dressed for the occasion. At the last possible moment John would mention that he had tickets, relying on my refusal, especially when I was breast-feeding Ann. Off he and Esther would go, and poor stupid mug, me, would feel happy to think my friend was going out to spend a pleasant evening.

Sometimes he would be civil enough to me before going out at night, but would land home in an awful fury. He would switch on my bedroom light calling on me to wake up to hear what he had to say: how he hated me; how he would never share a room with me again; how he wanted us to live separate lives.

I used to try to reason with him. It seemed to me that no man, especially one who was decently brought up and in his right senses, could go on like that. I was at my wits' end. He'd always been so kind and polite. I knew he wasn't secretly drinking because he hated drink. I was too innocent to realize that it was the natural reaction of a man torn in two by his conscience and his desires.

Queerly enough, I never thought of our marriage breaking up. I was heartbroken that my marriage, for all its promise, seemed to be taking the same line as my mother's. But John was basically so unlike my father that I kept on hoping that things would come right.

*

One evening he seemed to be in a thoughtful frame of mind. He told me over the dinner-table that he was going out but that he'd be home at nine o'clock. He asked me to wait up for him as he had something of importance to discuss with me.

I was delighted – John coming home early to have a talk with me! I wondered what it could be and tried to guess. Perhaps the change I'd longed for had really come. Perhaps he was going to agree to our moving to a house as far from his mother's as possible. All kinds of hopeful thoughts ran through my mind.

After putting the children to bed, I bathed, taking extra care with my appearance. Putting on a blue velvet dressing gown that John had once liked me to wear, I brushed my hair and tied it with a piece of blue ribbon. I was trembling with excitement as I waited for him.

As the clock struck nine I heard his footsteps on the front porch. I could hear his key chain tinkling as he fumbled for the lock. The door opened and closed with a crash. Then John was standing before me.

I had often seen him in a rage but this was different. It

seemed that he had really gone mad. He stood glaring, his face distorted. Without any preliminaries he shouted. 'Haven't I told you to get out!'

By now I had become thoroughly unnerved. I knew it was useless to try and reason with him, reminding him of his promise to have a talk with me as he had suggested earlier that night. So I said, 'John, what's come over you?'

He ignored my question and began a torrent of abuse. I appealed to him to be quiet and reminded him that the children were asleep, thinking that mention of them would quieten him.

All he said was: 'The children! What do I care about them! They're yours, and I hate you!'

'Why do you hate me? What have I done that you should hate me?' I was all at sea.

'Because you're standing in my way.'

'You must be mad.'

'Mad, am I?' he yelled. With that he rushed towards me and before I could do anything he pulled me off the lounge and threw me with full force against a china cabinet, shattering the glass doors. Everything in it was smashed to smithereens. My wrist was cut. I pressed my handkerchief to it to stop the bleeding without taking my eyes off his face.

He'd regained some of his self-control after this mad outburst, but his face remained a curious whitish-grey. He walked over to a table and took a cigarette from a pack that was lying there. He lit it and began to smoke. He talked more calmly now. I reproached him for going to sleep in the spare room. His answer was shattering. Blowing a cloud of smoke towards the ceiling and bringing his gaze back to my face he said, with a kind of pomposity – 'It isn't honourable for a man to sleep with one woman when he loves another.'

'What do you mean?' I was completely bewildered.

'I've already told you I love someone else.'

For an unsuspecting wife to be told by her husband that he loves another woman must always be a blow. My feelings must have shown clearly in my face. He looked at me, shrugged his shoulders, and said: 'Why look like that? After all, I'm not the first married man to love another woman. It happens in the best regulated families.'

I began to cry, although I had tried hard not to. Wiping away the tears with the sleeve of my gown I asked, 'Then you don't love me any more?'

'No,' he said decisively. He walked slowly over to the grate and ashed his cigarette.

'This woman,' I faltered, 'do I know her?'

'It's Esther,' he said.

I was thunderstruck. 'Esther! Oh, no! Not Esther! It couldn't be. Why she's my friend. She wouldn't do this to me.'

He shrugged again. 'Well you might as well get used to it, because it's true.'

'How long has this been going on?' My knees were trembling and I sat down.

'Oh, about six months I should say.' He spoke as calmly as if we were discussing a game of tennis.

'Does she know about this, about you telling me, I mean?'

'Yes, tonight we talked it over, and decided that we couldn't go on any longer this way. You'd have to be told.'

'So she sent you home to confess?'

'Look here, it's no use us going on like this any longer. You'll agree you haven't been very happy of late.'

'No, I haven't, because of the way you've neglected me.'

'Well, now you understand the position, I hope you'll be reasonable.'

'What do you want me to do?'

'If you'll stop snivelling long enough, I'll tell you what I propose. The Mater is a very generous person and is prepared to take the children and be responsible for their upbringing.'

'Does your mother know of all this? But I needn't ask. I don't believe you could make a single decision on your own.'

He shrugged and began pacing up and down the room.

'I wouldn't dream of parting with my children,' I said. 'Why, I couldn't bear to let anyone have them, least of all your mother.'

'What's wrong with my mother?' He bristled.

'Need we go into that?'

There was a silence while I waited for him to continue. He stopped pacing and stood before me.

'I'll compromise with you,' he paused, then continued: 'You take Ann with you and leave Terry here. Then I'll pay you what the law allows for you and the baby's support, but I warn you, any funny business then you'll not get a cent and you won't even have Ann.'

'I haven't any intention of parting with my children,' I answered flatly, adding sarcastically, 'And what do you propose to do?'

'Well, he said, rocking backwards and forwards on his heels, and seeming to enjoy the question, 'I haven't been up to par lately and the Mater thinks I should take a sea trip, salt air and all that sort of thing, you know.'

'Where does Esther fit into all this?'

'Oh, I intend taking her along with me.'

'Do you mean to tell me your mother knows of this arrangement, too?' I exclaimed incredulously.

'The Mater is only concerned with my happiness, so you'd better think it over.' With that he turned and walked out of the room.

I went to bed but couldn't sleep. I turned over everything in my mind, fully aware that John, backed, or perhaps even instigated, by his mother would do everything he said. I knew, too, that his mother would help him in every way possible no matter how irregular it might be.

Even if I had known anything of the law I had seen enough in associating with John and his mother that money was more powerful than right. I also knew that if he really tried to take the children from me his mother would stand by him with her money and influence. John may not have had any staying power but his mother certainly made up for it. I was terrified of the possibilities. John and his mother were too clever for me.

11

Apparently John didn't get in touch with Esther the next day, because she came to the house straight after work, just before he arrived home. I immediately tackled her. She was very cagey, until I told her that he'd confessed to me the night before. But she neither admitted or denied it. She was very obviously uneasy though, and kept watching the door waiting for John to come and take over.

Ann was sitting on a rug on the floor and Terry had been playing there alongside her. He jumped up and ran across to Esther and began to climb on her knee. He was very fond of her. She put him from her. I said something then about the children – what this breaking up of the home would mean for them. But she paid little heed to what I was saying, keeping her eyes on the door. I pleaded with her to think it over.

I remember I talked to her as though she intended going away with any other man and because she was my friend I didn't want to see her suffer. I talked quietly and without rancour. She was so ill at ease that it was plain she hadn't intended to see me again once I'd found out.

Suddenly she got up and went out; she'd heard the gate click, and I hadn't. She returned with John. Now she was very cocky. I dropped my pleading manner when I saw how she'd changed. I had plenty to say. I reminded her of what I'd done for her. I told her I'd given her the run of my home. I remember, as if it were yesterday, her standing there, her hands thrust into the pockets of her short coat.

She looked artfully up into John's face and retorted: 'You mean John's home.'

I began to get really angry. It was the last straw when she told me that I couldn't hold him; that it was just too bad, but she couldn't be worried. To put it bluntly I lost my block. I would have cheerfully killed her, but I couldn't even chance striking her as John's whole attitude showed that he was ready to throttle me if I laid a hand on his darling.

With it all, it still seemed like a bad dream from which I'd wake up. You see, I trusted them implicitly, and it was a terrible blow. Only the thought of the children kept me from running amok. As I stood looking at them, John glaring at me with hate in his eyes his arm round her shoulders, Esther standing beside him her head close to his, glossy black and silvery blond in startling contrast, a smile of triumph on her face, I knew that it was no accident, no temporary infatuation on her part. She'd wanted him all along. I was dazed with the shock of everything.

The full horror of it all only dawned on me when my mother-in-law came sailing through the connecting gates next morning. I was in the kitchen and saw her – dressed up to kill – cross the lawn with Martha Tuppa in attendance. I don't know whether she brought Martha as a bodyguard or as witness, but when I faced them across the lounge I was sickened to see the same gleam of triumph in their faces as in Esther's.

She had come with a cut-and-dried proposition about the children. She would see I got a weekly income for life.

I said, 'No.'

She began to bargain: same terms if I'd keep Ann and let her have Terry.

I said 'No' again.

I muttered something about a divorce and she pounced on me. She wouldn't have the name of Marsh dragged through the divorce court. She'd have no scandal. It has never been clear to me from that day to this what she was after. I could have understood it if Esther came of what my mother-in-law considered a good family, or if she'd had money.

Looking back on it I think she had a kind of long-term plan – let John go off with Esther without being married and he would tire of her as he had tired of me. Then he would come back to his mother. Her demand for Terry might have been based on affection. I sometimes thought that, to her, he was another John, to rear, to spoil, to hold. But I think it was also to spite me and hurt me. I've never really worked it out. Anyway, at that stage I'd got beyond even saying no. I just shook my head.

Then she began to threaten me. If I didn't give up the children without a fuss she'd take me to court. She'd bring witnesses to prove I was an unsuitable mother. Hadn't I gone out as a wet nurse and neglected my husband and son for sheer greed? Hadn't I connived at my husband going out with another woman? She could prove this. She could prove that. She reminded me of the case of the famous actress Emilie Polini* which had recently filled the papers.

I know it sounds incredibly stupid, but I believed that she was capable of putting every threat into action. And once up against the Law what chance had I if Emilie Polini had lost? I was the innocent party but so was she. And she was a rich woman with influence and reputation, while I. . . .

The little plump woman's threats and appeals only ceased when Ann woke up from her morning sleep and began to cry. I took her up and held her, shaking my head stubbornly at everything she said.

At last she got up and stamped out, with Martha scuttling after her like a black beetle. At the door Martha stopped and ran back. Her mouth was twitching and her boot-button eyes stared at me as she thrust her face against mine and

* The case of Emilie Polini made legal history in New South Wales. She was a celebrated actress, daughter of G. M. Polini who was manager of the old London Adelphi. In a case for the custody of her child, she lost. There was such a sustained clamour in Australia against the law which operated harshly against the mother that, years later, an Act – The Guardianship of Infants Act – remedied the position. Emilie Polini never knew – she had died several years earlier.

hissed rather than whispered: 'You'll be sorry.'

As I watched them go across the back lawn my mind was already made up. I decided to run away taking the children with me.

Next morning I told Terry that he must kiss his Daddy before he left for work.

'Why, Mummy?' he asked curiously.

I told him that because his Daddy had forgotten to kiss him of late and that he must be sure to remind his Daddy to kiss him that morning.

When John was ready to leave, Terry went over to him, saying, 'Daddy, I want you to kiss me before you go this morning.'

John bent down and kissed his little son. Then I moved over to him with Ann in my arms and held her forward for him to kiss her. He did so, looked briefly at me and then he turned and went swiftly down the front steps. I watched him turn the corner of our street and I thought to myself: Well, John Marsh, that's the last time you'll ever see your children again if I can help it.

I felt that he'd forfeited all rights to them, as he'd refused to leave his mother's purse strings for his babes and now he was preparing to sacrifice them and me for Esther.

I felt sure, too, that after what he had said to me and his disregard of the future of his children, that he was not worth fighting for.

I started to pack. I was aware that I would have to sneak the children away.

My mother-in-law was going out for a game of golf, but I still had Martha to contend with. When I'd finished packing I dressed the children and myself and then I rang for a cab.

Terry was excited at the prospect of going some place but I couldn't bring myself to tell him that we wouldn't be coming back and that he would not be seeing his father again.

When the cab arrived I hurried the children out to it while the cabby brought our luggage from the front porch. As the cab moved away I glanced back for a last look, for I knew I would never return.

Glancing at my mother-in-law's place I noticed a curtain at one of the windows fall back into place and I knew that Martha had seen us. I could well imagine her phoning John or his mother of what she had just seen. But I didn't care. I already felt free.

How they reacted to my going I never found out. Apparently they made no effort to track me down. They probably thought my going was better planned than it was, or maybe they were just glad to be rid of me so easily.

Sometimes, as I think of it now, I wonder if I was really in my right senses. I was twenty-three, and untrained for any sort of work that would bring me a decent living and I knew very little of the world. Besides, I hadn't any money except a few pounds I'd saved from my housekeeping funds.

There was no one I could turn to and I had nowhere to go. But I had my children and at the time that was all I thought of.

12

I had burnt my boats!

Directing the cabby to Central I checked our luggage until I could find a room. Then we started the trek. We tramped the streets for hours, Terry alternately running ahead and lagging behind. Ann, just learning to walk, had to be carried most of the time.

Doors were opened to us, but as soon as the children were spotted most were slammed in our faces. Some people were polite enough, others were indifferent but most were rude and insulting. There were no laws in those days to compel a landlord to let his premises to anyone with children.

It was late afternoon, and beginning to rain, when we finally came to a residential in Darlinghurst. It was a large, three-storied house huddled between a row of shops. Its front door led directly on to the footpath. Faded red linen blinds adorned the windows on either side of the door. The place was altogether shabby and dilapidated, but there was a notice in one of its windows, 'Room to let.'

I pushed the front door open to enter a long narrow hall, where several doors opened off on either side and at the extreme end was a stairway.

The first door on our right bore the sign 'Enquiries.' I sat the children down on the one chair and waited. Presently the door opened and a big woman dressed in black appeared. She had a mop of red, curly hair and about three chins. I told her

I needed accommodation for myself and the two children. Without waiting to take a breath I told her I was desperate and I hoped that she wouldn't turn me away.

Whether it was out of pity for me, or whether the room had been vacant for a long time, I don't know but she told me I could have it, provided I promised to keep the children quiet. I promised I would. She told me that all her tenants were good payers and she wouldn't have them disturbed.

The rent was thirty shillings a week, including electric light, and there was a penny-in-the-slot gas meter. I was to share the conveniences with another tenant. The rent was greater than I had expected to pay but the sun was already going down and I had no alternative. Getting thirty shillings out of my purse I handed it to her.

'Oh, yes – and there's two shillings deposit on the keys. You get that back when you leave – if you return the keys.' Then she added, 'It's number five flat on the second floor. You'll find your room at the end of the hall.'

We made our way up the stairs, Terry running on ahead. I had to restrain him, as I didn't want to create a bad impression right away. We arrived at the landing of the second floor. The smell that hit my nostrils suggested escaping gas mixed with the smell of rank cooking-fat. Before I could reach for the electric switch Terry had collided with the battered old garbage tin standing at the top step. The light shone feebly, being nothing more than a pilot-light. First door on our right opened into the bathroom, the next opening was the kitchenette. Next to that was a bedroom already tenanted. The remaining door beyond it must be ours. I opened it and we entered.

Well, it certainly was a dump. The light was just another pilot-globe. Dark furniture and drab curtains added to the gloom, whilst ventilation had apparently been unheard of by the architects.

I sat Ann on the only chair in the room, then turned and opened the window. My hands were covered with dust from the window-frame, and I thought a good dusting was the least the place needed. From the window I looked down on a narrow street, little more than a lane, bordered on either side by tiny slum dwellings which seemed to lean on each other in their efforts to defy the law of gravity. It seemed incredible that people lived and mated in such hovels.

All this time Terry had been running about exploring, thinking our new home, as he called it, was good fun. I turned from the window just in time to see him climb up on to the bed and reach for the light-switch, which consisted of a piece of string and several bootlaces knotted together. It was drawn across the room and fastened to the head of the bed, probably an invention of a previous tenant to save getting out of bed to switch off the light. On the bed was a near-silk spread, which may have been yellow once upon a time but now had that dirty washed-out appearance I have since come to associate with all furnished rooms. There were several lumps in the mattress. It certainly was in keeping with the rest of the furniture. The bedroom suite was a two-piece affair – odd pieces. When I attempted to open the combined wardrobe and dressing-table, this plywood monstrosity almost toppled forward on to me. After some struggling I managed to get the ill-fitting door open. I decided not to try and open the drawers until later.

The walls alongside the bed were spattered with dirty stains, as though someone had been swatting mosquitoes. Pulling back the bedclothes I found the mattress covered with dirty, yellow stains, as though it had been frequently wetted, and there were holes where the buttons had once been, allowing the dubious kapok to poke through in places. I stripped the bedclothes off the bed and immediately took them down to the landlady, explaining that, as I had my own, I would not be needing them. I said I hoped she would not be offended. On the contrary, she seemed very pleased, saying, 'That's all right. They'll come in handy for another tenant.'

Thinking the children would be safe for a few minutes, I went out on to the street and hailed a passing cab. Handing the driver my luggage checks I asked him to pick my cases up at Central and bring them to me. You could do that with cabs in those days. I had been wise enough to bring my portable sewing-machine and a rug. As the cab, one of those that looked like a yellow mustard-pot, moved away I turned to go inside. A dirty-looking character leered at me and tried to bar my path. He said in low tones, 'What's it worth kid?' I ran around him in sudden panic.

I burst breathlessly into our room to find that Ann had climbed off her chair and was now inspecting the poky little grate. Her frock, a cream woollen one I had knitted for her, was covered in soot. Terry was not in the room. I hurried out into the hall calling him.

'Here I am, Mummy,' came from the kitchenette. I walked

in to find that he had turned on all the gas-jets and was covered in grease from the filthy stove.

I set to and started cleaning the place as best I could, starting on the kitchenette. Nothing more than a cubicle, it held a small pine table, two chairs with nothing in common apart from their habit of twisting from under you when sat on, a cupboard and a small gas-stove and, for some reason, a hair broom with no hair in it. The contents of the cupboard were a revelation! A few odd pieces of crockery, cracked and chipped, and two battered saucepans with holes where the handles had once been. This assortment appeared to have been unwashed for years. After trying to brighten up the stove by cleaning off the ancient and peeling paint and as much of the grease as possible, I stood back and surveyed the room. Damp and peeling walls adequately set off the picture of this 'dining-room'. Deciding that nothing could be done there until I could get a scrubbing brush and carbolic, I went and inspected the bathroom.

This was in keeping with the rest of the place. It contained a rather good bath which, however, was in a filthy condition, with grease-marks graduating around the sides and brown stains here and there as though indiscriminate use had been made of Condy's Crystals. An old-fashioned bath heater gave doubtful promise of a bath – if one could get the filth cleaned out of it. In one corner stood the W.C., a piece of rope hanging dejectedly in place of a chain. In another corner stood two brooms in no better condition than the one in the kitchenette, a bucket and a filthy mop. The long, narrow window had been painted green as a concession to modesty, but was long overdue for another coat of paint, if only to obscure the obscene writings scratched on it.

After giving the children their tea and putting them to bed I spent another hour cleaning up, then went to bed exhausted. The mattress creaked and sagged and I had the feeling of lying uphill. It was as much as I could do to stop myself from falling to the floor.

The children who had always slept by themselves now tossed and turned fretfully. I put on the light to see if I could do anything to make them comfortable. On looking closely I noticed red lumps on their arms and legs, and then saw some tiny whitish-looking mites crawling on the bed. Horrified, I turned Ann over and saw some bigger ones, brown in colour. I had never seen a bug in my life but I had no doubt that these awful things were bugs, and realized at once that the heat had caused them to come out.

I lifted the children on to the floor, and could see that the bed was crawling. I thought desperately of something to do, and remembered the bedroom next door had been vacated soon after we arrived. Maybe there was a clean mattress in there.

Covering the sleeping children on the floor, I hurried along and tried the bedroom door, but it was locked. I went into the kitchenette and leaned out into the light-well. Thank heavens! The window was open and I climbed out onto the sewerage pipe which ran horizontally beneath the windows. It seemed to take hours for me to edge my way that few feet along to the open window. Clambering into the room I found the switch and turned on the light. The mattress seemed quite clean. I hastily bundled it up and carried it across the room. Opening the yale lock, I struggled out and along to our bedroom. A few minutes and the exchange had been effected and none the wiser. I felt sure the landlady would never know, for I doubt if she ever came higher than the ground floor.

I went to sleep that night wondering how many bugs were wandering about looking for their mattress. The place would have to be thoroughly cleaned out the next day, I thought, as I drifted to sleep.

In my cramped postion beside the children, sleep seemed almost impossible. The fetid smell was smothering. I'd never in my life been a place like this.

Sleepless and exhausted my problems chased themselves round in my mind. I thought of the home I had been forced to leave; my bedroom with its cream walls and highly polished furniture. . . . The low frilly chair . . . the hassock beside it where I used to rest my feet while I sat feeding my babies. . . . The wide glassed-in verandah off my room where the children slept . . . and the green lawns beyond it where they romped and played. . . . Should I have taken them from it all? Wouldn't it perhaps have been better to leave them where they would at least have been well-cared for? Then I remembered John's complete indifference to them. I was quite convinced he'd only wanted them because his mother had put the idea into his head.

Women might come and women might go in John's fickle heart but he'd always go home to his mother.

Remembering her cruel blue eyes I knew I was right.

Whatever my children might have to do without they would have love.

Somewhere across the street in one of the tiny hovels came the weak cry of a sick child, and then the soothing voice of a woman. . . .

Apparently I must have dozed off for I was awakened by two women who were fighting underneath my window. From their conversation I gathered that they were prostitutes and one was accusing the other of having poached on her beat.

Just about every swear word had passed between them when suddenly there was the noise of a window being flung open and a man's voice called out.

'Hey there, if it's all the same to youse I'd like ter git some sleep.'

The noise and language continued until a voice further along the street called.

'Look out girls, here comes the coppers!'

There was the sound of running footsteps – then silence. . . . I dozed off and didn't hear any more until I was awakened at dawn by a milk cart as it clattered past the window.

Wearily I gazed around at the discoloured walls and shabby furniture which looked even more shoddy in the grey morning light.

In the kitchenette I found the table littered with the remains of a prawn supper and two empty beer bottles.

So this was what sharing conveniences meant. I had thought that my neighbour whom I had yet to meet, would have co-operated with me when she saw how clean the place was, but apparently she took it for granted – if she ever noticed it!

That morning a baker called to get my custom, and I arranged that he leave me a loaf each day. As he was leaving I asked him if he knew of anyone locally who might agree to mind the children for me during the day. He said that he didn't know of anyone, but that he'd keep his eye open.

The rest of that day I spent in cleaning out the bedroom with disinfectant.

Next morning I found a note pinned to our door. It was from the baker telling me he had found a woman prepared to mind the children. He had written down her address, saying to go around as soon as I could. After breakfast I dressed the children and we set out to see Mrs Platt, for that was the woman's name.

13

It was a lovely day after the rain of the night before and my
spirits rose as we made our way through the narrow streets
and laneways, eventually finding Wiley Street, the street
mentioned in the baker's note. It was a narrow street and
dwindled into a lane-way. Terraces lined both sides, reminding me of the view from our bedroom window, except that
Wiley Street featured the two-storey type of terrace, with
front verandahs abutting on to the footpaths, here and there
separated by dirty, grey wooden fences nearly devoid of palings.
My spirits fell. This was hardly an environment in which to
leave my children, but I supposed the baker would hardly
have sent me here if the people weren't all right.

Looking for the number of Mrs Platt's house, I noticed that
some windows were neatly curtained and washed clean, while
others were shabby and had that smoky look from the want
of water. I glanced up at a balcony, one end of which was
partitioned off for a cooking space, judging by the saucepans
which could be seen through the narrow slit that served as a
door. At the other end of the balcony was a stretcher, partly
obscured by a grey, weather-stained canvas blind whose tattered
ends flapped slightly in the breeze.

Finally we came to Mrs Platt's house, and as I pushed open
the iron gate I looked back down the street in time to see a
dead cat being scooped on to a shovel and tossed on to the
garbage cart.

I raised the old cast-iron knocker and tapped Mrs Platt's
door gently. This produced a shuffling noise from the depths
of the house, followed by the sound of the lock being snapped
back. This was Mrs Platt.

I explained that the baker had given me her address and
for what purpose. Without saying a word she drew back and
indicated that we were to enter with an eloquent jerk of her
thumb over the shoulder. It was a room of the type known as
an open front room, popular in tenement houses, for it dis-
penses with the need for a hall and saves valuable space --

54

valuable in the landlord's building costs, of course.

Along the wall facing the front door stood a new and expensive looking pianola, uncomfortably out of place among the wax flower ornaments and gaudy furnishings surrounding it. Piled high on top of it was a mountain of music-rolls in untidy confusion. Crowded into the tiny room was a worn settee, and at Mrs Platt's direction I sat down with Ann on my lap, and Terry seated beside me. Mrs Platt flopped into an easy chair opposite me, breathing heavily. She accomplished this manoeuvre with difficulty, for she was a big woman with arms like legs of mutton. Her hair was black and hung lank about her face. Pushing it back behind her ears, she began talking. From where I was sitting I had a good view of her, and sat quietly studying her as she talked. I came to the conclusion almost at once that she wasn't the type I would choose to look after my children, but I had no choice at the moment. I consoled myself that it wouldn't be for long.

'Yes,' Mrs Platt was saying, 'my five kids goes to school, so these little pets will be company for me of a day. You'll have a good 'ome 'ere with me,' she gushed to the children. She said the children could play with her kids' toys while they were at school.

I explained that I would bring them in the mornings and pick them up each evening after work. She agreed to give them their dinner and tea, and then we approached the subject of payment.

To my question what she would charge for this she frowned, made a clicking noise with tongue and looked up at the ceiling as though she was working out a weighty mathematical problem. A few 'Ahs' and 'Hmmmms,' then she looked back at me. 'What d'yer say to a pound a week?' Before I had time to speak she went on to explain that she would have to get extra fruit and milk, 'As the little pets would get nothin' but the best at my table.'

I agreed to one pound per week, although I was wondering how I would be able to find that amount each week. I had no idea what kind of work I would be able to get, much less how much my wages would be. Mrs Platt said she would like the money in advance, so I gave her a pound note.

Ann was beginning to lose her earlier shyness and began pulling at the curtains behind me. I decided it was time to be going and rose with Ann in my arms, while Terry, who had been very quiet and well-behaved, clung firmly to my skirt.

Mrs Platt eased herself out of her chair and opened the door for us. I said goodbye to her, saying that I would leave the children first thing in the morning, and we made our way down the street deserted save for two urchins riding a billy-cart along the footpath. Somehow I was suddenly depressed and irritable and could not blame Terry for showing signs of fretting. Ann was too young, of course, to understand the object of our visit. That night I explained to Terry that I would have to go to work every day to keep him and his little sister, but Terry had different views.

'I don't want to go and stay in that lady's place, Mummy, I want you to take us home to Daddy, Mummy. I don't like this place – it's a dirty old place.'

The novelty had worn off and this was the moment I had been dreading.

'We won't be going home to Daddy – ever,' I told him. He wanted to know why but I told him he would know when he grew up to be a big boy.

'Now,' I said, 'you've got to help Mummy. You're my little man, and I want you to look after Ann while Mummy's at work.' He listened quietly and promised that he would. But he was only a baby and I knew that he would forget this promise as soon as I left him at Mrs Platt's.

Next morning I took them to stay their first day with her. Although Terry fought hard to hold back the tears, I knew he would cry as soon as I had gone. I slipped away without Ann realizing I was going.

After leaving them I made my way into town to sell my engagement ring, and came to a murky little shop with the traditional three balls hanging outside, and a large sign announcing that the benevolent owner would lend you one pound for sixpence. I had decided to sell it to keep us going for a while, although I didn't like the idea of parting with it. But that all belonged to the past, I told myself – and the few pounds in my purse wouldn't last forever. Still I fingered my ring reluctantly.

A short and very fat little man stared at me across a mountain of old golf-clubs, banjos, boxing-gloves, field-glasses and other treasures. Taking the ring from my finger I handed it across to him, saying I wished to sell it. He grunted as he held it to the light for inspection, then asked me how much I wanted for it.

I thought it had cost thirty pounds, so I said: 'Thirty pounds.'

He threw back his head and laughed, displaying a lot of gold teeth.

'Thirty pounds – are you choking?'

I replied that I was not joking, and that the ring had cost thirty pounds.

'Yeth, it might haf – but how long ago? The market – it hath fallen thinth then.'

'Very well, I'll try somewhere else,' I said, holding out my hand for the ring, but he held it away from me.

'Look, I gif you eighteen pounds for it. An' then I thow a loth.'

I opened my mouth to say no, but hesitated. After all, he might be right, I pondered. I didn't know anything about precious stones. So I said, 'All right, eighteen pounds.' And eighteen pounds it was.

The next thing to do was to find myself a job. Buying a *Herald*, I looked through the Situations Vacant columns not too sure of what to look for, as job-seeking was quite a new experience for me. One advertisement held my attention. It stated that a well-known firm of tea shops required waitresses, with or without experience, and gave the address in the city at which applicants would be interviewed.

Well, I was interviewed and so became a waitress for thirty shillings per week, at one of the firm's branch shops in the city. I was to start work the next morning. The wages were not enough to live on, but I reasoned that I would just have to carry on, drawing on the money I'd raised on the ring, until I could find a better job paying more money. With a pound for Mrs Platt, and thirty shillings per week to be found for the rent, breakfast for the children and myself, plus fares to and from work, with other incidentals, my few pounds wouldn't last very long. Although I was to have some of my meals at the shop, that wouldn't help very much. But I had the optimism of youth and felt certain that something would turn up.

14

Next morning I arrived at the tea shop punctually at seven-thirty. An elderly woman was busily scrubbing the floor; she glanced up as I asked her the way to the staff dressing-room.

Tossing the hair from her moist face she waved a soapy hand towards a room at the back of the shop.

I thanked her, and stepping carefully on the damp floor through rows of marble-topped tables stacked high with chairs, I felt that I was already launched in the busy working world as I opened the door and went in.

It was a small room and had evidently been a pantry, but now served as a dressing-room for the staff. I noticed that there was only one chair and a sink – the only amenities provided.

A group of women were chatting in desultory fashion as they changed from their street clothes into black dresses and stiffly starched white aprons. Apart from a cursory glance in my direction they paid little attention to me as they hung their clothes on nails around the wall.

I began to change and looked around for somewhere to hang my dress but there wasn't a spare nail to be seen, so I hung it on the back of the chair, then followed my work-mates out to the dining-room, where a woman called Clara, the head waitress, gave me a list of my duties.

I began by setting up tables and serving an occasional customer until noon when business became brisk:

The customers, who were mostly employees of surrounding business houses, flocked to the tables, everyone wanting to be served at once.

The food was good, but the service was only third-rate, yet the place was packed to overflowing. My feet ached and burned as though I was walking on hot coals.

The constant clatter of crockery and the noise of the waitresses as they bawled their orders to the kitchen played havoc with my already frayed nerves. I developed a headache.

Because of my inexperience and the fact that some of the waitresses snatched the food I had ordered I became hopelessly confused.

My customers naturally became impatient and one man who had been waiting half an hour for a steak lost his temper and went red in the face until the veins stood out above his collar. I tried to explain that another waitress had taken his order, but he jumped up from his seat and brushing me aside, grabbed his hat from a peg on the wall and stamped out muttering to himself.

After the lunch rush was over I began clearing off tables, carrying tray loads of dirty dishes to the kitchen until I thought I'd snap in two.

At two o'clock I sat down to lunch which consisted of a pie and a bread roll.

Within half an hour I was back on the floor again cleaning silver, or serving when it became busy. I watched the clock on the wall, but the big hand never seemed to move. It was the longest afternoon I've ever known.

At seven o'clock the doors were closed to business. At a quarter to eight I followed my workmates to the dressing-room. There was a stampede as everyone seemed in a hurry to get off the premises. I looked around for my frock where I'd left it on the back of the chair, but it had fallen to the floor and had been trampled on.

Clara was waiting outside the dressing-room door, and as we filed out she made a thorough search of our bags. I found that this was a rule that was rigidly carried out.

I thought it was pretty tough working eleven and a half hours for thirty shillings a week, and suffering the ignominy of having one's bag searched! But in those days there was little Union organization and it was not until some years later that a campaign by the Union resulted in decent conditions being won.

My feet still ached and burned, as I limped along dark side streets and back lanes to collect my babies.

It seemed I was to have my troubles at the tea shop. The manageress, a coarse old female, forever strutting about the place with what she no doubt imagined to be a regal air, made my job almost intolerable. She was mean and petty, and showed her dislike for me by continually giving me the jobs no one else liked doing. However, I think she knew the feeling was mutual.

She had her pets, of course, and they would hang around her bringing flowers or other small presents for her. One waitress, with a little more enterprise than the others, even made undies for her! She was a poor waitress, always behind with her work. I've noticed, time and again, that people given to crawling to the boss are seldom good workers. No doubt it is their way of keeping their jobs.

There was one little waitress working with me whom I liked and we became firm friends. Her name was Josie, and she had jet-black hair and big blue eyes which gave her a babyish look and a disarming smile went with it. She reminded me of a doll. I understood her to be married, and that her husband worked on a boat.

The weeks flew into months; summer came and time was running out on me and my money. But I was still working at the tea shop, getting no time to look around for a better job.

Then it came! One day a regular customer came into lunch. He was a little man who always wore a buttonhole and invariably had something bright to say when he came in. He would talk about racehorses to anyone who cared to listen, and I gathered that he depended on them for his living. This day we were talking when he suddenly said:

'Why don't you get a job in a pub? You're much too attractive to spend your life serving pies.'

I replied that it didn't matter what one sold, as long as one was paid for doing it.

'But you'd get nearly twice as much pulling beer,' he protested.

The manageress called me away before I could answer, but he'd given me something to think about. Up till then my knowledge of pubs was nil, but for the rest of the day I thought of my prospects of finding a job in an hotel.

At knock-off time I made a quick decision: I asked for my pay. I got it – less two days in lieu of notice.

The day had been very hot and I felt weary as I made my way to collect the children.

When I'd put them to bed I carried the sewing-machine into the kitchenette to do some sewing. The night was stifling, without a breath of wind, alhough I had the window wide open. It faced a brick wall, and did not admit much air at any time.

Tiring from sewing, I put the machine away and was about to go to bed when Josie called. I had invited her to come and visit me if she ever had a spare night with nothing to do. I was both surprised and glad to see her. I put the light out so as not to disturb the children, and took her into the kitchenette.

I drew up a chair for her, warning her to sit down gently in case it collapsed. She rested her elbows on the table and nodded towards the other bedroom: 'Business as usual in there?'

Something in the tone of her voice made me glance at her quickly. 'What do you mean?'

Josie sniffed. 'Don't tell me you don't know what's going on here?'

'What do you mean?' I asked again, bewildered.

'They're mostly prostitutes living here. Everyone in the

district knows that. Some of them have their bludgers living here with them, too. Or living *off* them, I should say. I'll bet the noise you hear late at night is one of them beating his woman up for not bringing in enough money.'

'Good gracious,' I exclaimed. 'I had no idea.'

'Now you know, do you think it's a fit place for your kids? Or you, either, for that matter?'

'No, but it was the only place I could find at the time.'

'Well, now that you're a wake-up, why don't you try and find somewhere decent to live?'

'But it isn't as easy as all that. People don't like children, you know.'

'When you get a bit of time off you want to go around and have a look. There must be a few about who wouldn't mind having the kids.'

Next morning I bought a *Herald* and there it was in the Wanted Column. 'Smart attractive young woman to learn the bar. Apply "World's Agency".' Going over to the mirror, I looked at my reflection and thought to myself that I measured up to the requirements. H'm, attractive enough, but it hadn't helped me to hold my husband, I thought bitterly.

As I boarded a city-bound tram, I felt excited and yet apprehensive – the usual symptoms of job-hunting, I supposed.

15

My heart was in my throat as I stood outside a door marked World's Employment Agency. I knocked timidly, and a voice bade me enter. Then I was inside and a woman was seated at a desk, busily reading some letters. Apparently she had just arrived for she still had her hat on. I sat down and waited. It looked as though I was the first applicant, and I felt hopeful.

Presently the sound of footsteps came from the stairs, and several men and women entered and took seats near me. Gradually the room began to fill up, until no more could get in and a crowd accumulated around the door. The woman at the desk nodded to several and they said good morning to her.

An old woman sitting next to me began talking to me, telling that she was a cleaner, usually doing offices. She started to tell me her troubles – how her son had recently married and that she couldn't get along with his wife. 'So I got out and I'm fendin' fer meself,' she said.

I looked at her wrinkled old face and gnarled hands, calloused and work-worn, and wondered what sort of a man her son could be to let his mother go scrubbing floors.

Madam was now removing her hat and looking as though she might get down to business. She turned and looked us over. Her face reminded me of suet, and it was obvious she wore a wig. It was white, and fluffed around her ears. Her arms were laden with Nellie Stewart bangles, from one of which dangled a metal season ticket. The phone rang, and Madam's bangles tinkled as she reached for it. There was a hum of voices, with everyone seeming to talk at once, and Madam lifted her head and shushed the crowd to silence. Everyone stopped at once – to listen to Madam's conversation. It seemed that the caller was not offering a job, so the hum of voices started almost immediately.

As Madam hung up I rose and nervously crossed over to her. I told her I had come in answer to the advertisement for someone to learn the bar. She asked where I had worked before and why I had left. I told her I had left my last job because I wanted to become a barmaid. This seemed a satisfactory explanation to her, for she said: 'Well, go and sit down. My client will be in for interviews at ten-thirty.'

There was a movement of excitement as a new arrival entered. There was a faint fragrance of some expensive perfume. She was very small, and was dressed in a grey, well-fitting costume, with a tiny, black hat perched over one eye and a squirrel choker. Altogether a pleasing sight.

Madam rose from her chair and came forward to greet her ingratiatingly. Obviously this was no job-seeker! 'Good morning, Mrs Smith – do come and sit down,' said Madam, and led the way to a tiny cubicle, holding back the cretonne curtain for Mrs Smith to enter. Madam followed and the curtain fell back into place. This must be the client Madam was expecting at ten-thirty, I decided.

I'd seen several girls speak to Madam earlier, and wondered if they were after the same job as I. I began to feel nervous. A few minutes passed, then Madam poked her head out through the curtained door and beckoned to me. I squeezed into the cubicle and found myself in the presence of my prospective employer. Close up to her now I could see that her hair was hennaed and her face was hard and lined. But she had a nice manner as she proceeded to ask me questions about myself, and if I thought I'd like bar-work. I wanted to say I did not know as I had never worked in a bar, but instead I answered, 'Oh, yes, I'd love it.'

Madam interrupted with: 'Take off your hat and let Mrs Smith have a good look at you.'

Mrs Smith raised a gloved hand in protest and said, smiling: 'Certainly not. Indeed, I wouldn't expect anyone to take off their hat without first consulting a mirror.'

The smile she sent in my direction made me feel at ease right away.

Madam then asked her if she would like to interview any more applicants who were waiting outside, but Mrs Smith spoke decisively: 'No thank you – this young lady will suit me nicely.'

Turning to me she said: 'The wages will be two pounds ten to start with and a rise of ten shillings when you become experienced.' She then said, 'Do you think you could start in a day or two?'

I replied that I could start next morning if it suited her.

Thinking of the loss of wages made me anxious to start as soon as possible. Mrs Smith apparently thought my eagerness was a sign of enthusiasm at the prospect of learning the bar and this seemed to please her.

'Very well then, tomorrow at eight-thirty. You'll have one afternoon off through the week and, of course, all day Sundays. Oh, yes, and you'll live out of course.' She proceeded to give me directions as to how to reach the hotel – which tram to catch, and where to get out.

Madam then asked me to wait outside.

Presently Mrs Smith came out and gave me an encouraging smile as she went past me out of the office.

Madam went over to her desk asking me to follow. 'The fee will be ten shillings,' she told me and wrote out a receipt as I got the money out of my purse.

As I walked out the door a little man propped against the wall said: 'Finished with yer paper, Miss?'

I handed it to him, although it had cost a penny and every penny counted. But it had brought me luck and I hoped the day would never come when I wouldn't have a penny for a paper.

16

I've already told you about my first day in the bar. That day
I went home feeling that I would never go back to it again.
But I went. Beggars can't be choosers – particularly beggars
with babies!

It wasn't much of a pub to look at. Just a small place on a
corner in a drab side street running up from the wharves. But
the Missus liked me and was very kind and helpful. The customers turned out to be much better than I'd thought them
the first day. The pay was better and the work no harder than
that of a waitress once I learned the ropes. And the tips made
a difference. In short, I got used to the bar as one gets used to
anything. That second day I began to learn the routine of the
place.

The old derelict was in his usual place as soon as we opened.
A few regulars drifted in and out. About the middle of the
morning a fine-looking man came in, dressed much better
than the majority of our customers. He called good-day to
the useful and came over to where I stood, leaned on the
counter, and ordered a pony of lager.

I felt uncomfortable, as I didn't know what he meant by a
pony. Apparently he read my thoughts, for he drew my attention to a row of small lady's waist glasses and said: 'Use one of
those, Miss.'

His obviously admiring stocktaking of me filled me with
embarrassment as I served him, almost making me drop the
bottle as I lifted the seal. As I set the drink before him he
threw a sporting paper on to the counter and pushed his hat
back on his head.

'Nice day, Caddie,' he drawled.

'What was that you called me?' I asked, surprised.

'I called you Caddie.'

'Why? That's not my name,' I said, feeling foolish.

'No, but it fits you to a tee,' he smiled.

'Wherever did you dig that up?'

'See that car out there?'

64

I looked and could see the bonnet of a very big car standing at the kerb.

'See her? Well, that's a Cadillac and she's mine.'

'Really?' I said, trying to appear as though I was not particularly interested.

'Yes, she's an eight cylinder job and the best Yank car on the market.'

'I don't see what that has to do with me.'

'You're like her – an eight cylinder job, and a beauty. So I'm calling you Caddie.'

'Oh,' I said, trying to show I was not a bit impressed at his compliment.

The name stuck, however, and soon all the customers were calling me Caddie, and even Mrs Smith. That name stuck to me right down through the years.

Mrs Smith came into the bar and smiled a greeting to my admiring stranger.

'Hello, Ted.'

He replied cheerily, finished his drink, smiled a cheerio to me, and left the bar.

'That's the S.P. bookie – he's a nice chap,' Mrs Smith informed me as she walked along to fill the old derelict's glass once again.

Soon it was lunch time, when business began to get brisk. Just on twelve there was a rush from all directions, mostly workers from the factories nearby. A few ate their lunches at the bar, whilst some sat on stools along the walls. There was a steady hum of voices as they washed their pies and sandwiches down with draughts of beer.

I heard several make wisecracks about the new barmaid, and one wag said: 'She ain't a bad sort of a sheila, Missus.'

The useful and the manager put in an appearance and the hour soon passed. Then the bar cleared, except for the old derelict, who was quite a fixture. As the useful took the broom out and started to sweep the scraps of food and waste paper scattered about the floor, I knocked off for lunch.

The second day ended like the first, and after that I settled down in my job, determined to learn the bar and make a success of it. Like any other occupation, it had its good points and its bad. For instance, the things customers sometimes say to barmaids are unprintable, but one just has to learn to take it. Some publicans won't tolerate having their girls insulted, but there are those who adopt the customer-is-always-right principle. However, if the barmaid was always running to the boss complaining of the insults she received, she'd get no work done.

Yes, I gradually got used to it. I even got used to the 'Ladies' Parlour'. While some of these women were tough and hard just for the sake of it, I did not dislike them. They nearly all had a tale to tell. I felt sorry for them instead of condemning them for drinking heavily and losing their self-respect as I had been inclined to do at first.

I was beginning to see that there was a lot more unhappiness in the world than I had realized, and that there were people with troubles that made mine seem insignificant. Happy people don't need the false comfort of liquor.

Smith's pub mightn't be much to look at but it was a goldmine so far as the bar trade went. Indeed, it did nothing but sell liquor, though the Licensing Laws required it to have bedrooms to let to the public and serve meals to travellers. But the rooms – like those in 90 per cent of the pubs in which I worked – were never even opened, much less let, and I really believe the Missus would have fainted if anyone had come in and asked for board and lodging.

The first week I spent learning how to pull beer and handle drunks. On my first afternoon off, I would have liked to have taken the children to the Gardens for the afternoon, but decided to get my washing done and so leave Sunday free. Sunday was the day I had been allotted as my day for the laundry.

After collecting the children from Mrs Platt I took them home. I gathered our soiled linen together, gave Terry the pegs and soap to carry and we all went downstairs to the laundry. Someone else had beaten me to it and was already at the tubs. It was the woman who lived in the room directly beneath ours – a hard-faced slattern whose Saturday night brawling with her man kept us awake. They may have lacked a good many things down there, but liquor was not one of them. As I approached the wash-house door, she glanced in my direction. I smiled and said 'Good afternoon' and passed a joking remark about her having beaten me to it. Glaring at me with watery eyes – one was black, I noticed – which did not match her wispy, peroxided hair wrapped in curling-papers, she jerked a peg from her mouth and snarled: 'Get to buggery out of 'ere while y're safe – and take yer bloody brats with yer!'

She took the wind right out of my sails!

'Don't you dare talk to me like that!' I gasped.

'And what might *you* be goin' ter do about it, eh? I'd like ter know!' she leered, squeezing a pairs of pants with tobacco stained fingers.

I was scared stiff. Without answering I turned away. It was no use getting into a brawl with this tough-egg, I decided.

As we started up the stairs she shouted: 'An' keep them bloody brats quiet or there'll be somethin' doin' – d'ya hear me?'

So that was why she was nasty. I made up my mind to find somewhere else to live somehow, and to keep the children exceptionally quiet for the rest of the time we were there. After visiting all the Estate Agents nearby without any luck, I decided to try a little further afield.

Walking along a street in the next suburb, a sign caught my eye – whitewashed letters on a piece of dealboard nailed to a post on the verandah, stating that a room was to let. I stood and surveyed the place. Peeling and weather-stained walls, with a window-pane here and there pasted over with brown paper, did not enhance its appearance. The house was surrounded with weed-grown gardens. I went in the gate and up the path. I glimpsed a stable at the rear of the house. An old grey horse was munching slowly at a manger nailed to the fence.

A slovenly woman answered my knock, a woman with unusually large hips far out of proportion to the rest of her body. The white sandshoes and black cashmere stockings suited her legs, which were beef to the ankles.

I asked about the room to let, explaining that there were three of us. To my relief she pulled the door open wide and shoved half a house-brick against it with her foot. Inviting us inside she said there was a room she was thinking of letting, if I cared to see it.

Mrs Norris, that was her name, opened a door off the hall and stood to one side, saying: 'This is it here.' It wasn't much better than the room we were already in, and it smelt musty, as though it had been closed up for a long time. A large, varnished wardrobe stood against one wall, and a dressing-table to match stood alongside an iron double bed badly in need of paint.

'The rent's a pound a week,' she informed me. 'And you can have the use of the kitchen.'

I asked her if she minded me doing my washing on Sundays, as I worked through the week. She replied that it didn't matter to her when I did my washing, so long as I didn't do it on Monday, that being her wash-day.

'But I won't have any men callers – you understand,' she said decidedly.

'You needn't worry about that,' I laughed. 'I haven't any men friends.'

She nodded approvingly, then went on to tell me that her husband had a vegetable run, that he kept his fruit and vegetables in the shed in the backyard and she hinted that it would be appreciated if I bought my requirements from him and that it would be cheaper for me. We went through the house to view the kitchen. It was in keeping with the rest of the place – a dingy, brown-walled little room with only a gas-jet to brighten the gloom. At one end stood a fuel stove; this, with a large table and half a dozen chairs, left very little space. Holes worn in the oilcloth covering the table gave me some idea of its age. This was where we would have our meals.

There was silence while she awaited my decision. 'I'll take the room,' I said, and opened my purse. Handing her a pound note I told her I'd move in at the week-end. I said goodbye and we left.

Well, I told myself, it's a respectable enough place, judging by the tone of Mrs Norris, who won't allow men callers.

That evening, as I came home with the children, I noticed the landlady's door ajar. Hearing us, she came out. It was obvious that she'd been waiting for us to arrive, for she immediately asked me why I couldn't keep the children quiet. I guessed that the peroxided slattern in the room beneath us had laid a complaint, but I was too tired to stop and explain or argue.

'I thought I told you when I let the place that you'd have to keep those children quiet,' she said, and went on coldly, 'I think you'd better find another place.'

I was thankful then that I had found Mrs Norris's room, and I said, 'As a matter of fact I already have another place, and we'll be leaving here at the week-end.'

She turned away, retorting, 'That suits me fine. See that you leave the place like you found it.'

'I can't do that,' I retorted, with unexpected courage, 'but I'll leave it clean, if that's what you mean.'

I started to trudge up the stairs, carrying Ann. Well, there's no doubt about it, I told myself, prostitutes and their bludgers have priority in this place.

17

The following Saturday was Election Day and I was looking forward to the day off, this being one of the rare days when all hotels were closed by law. Imagine my disappointment when the Missus told me to come in. I grumbled to myself but never in those early days thought of making a fuss with the Missus. I found it was a case of business as usual via the side door.

A cockatoo* in an alpaca coat and white sandshoes was posted on the pub corner, and the useful, guarding the door, admitted the customers. These would file silently into the bar in twos and threes and line the counter in silence. Glasses and bottles were handled carefully at first, but as the customers began to get a glow up, discretion went with the rest of their troubles and a hum soon mounted to a loud noise. The useful went around asking the customers to keep their voices down.

I was perspiring with the heat and humidity of the closed bar and was wishing myself out of it when the cockatoo tapped his signal on the side door – he had sighted a policeman in the distance. The boss signalled for me to stop serving, and the customers filed out the door after hurriedly gulping their beers. The last of them out, the useful closed the door and shot the bolts, and then came behind the counter to give me a hand to clean up. The Missus went for a late breakfast.

Knocking by the cockatoo indicated all-clear and the bar was soon filled again. Business was brisk. After two hours the draught beer gave out. The customers once more emptied into the street, more leisurely this time and some more tipsily.

Thankfully I started to clean up, thinking I would be able to get away early after all, but the demand for liquor was still strong, and I was kept busy running backwards and forwards from the bar to the door with bottles of beer, which the useful

* *Cockatoo*: A scout posted by publicans who do out-of-hours trading to warn of the approach of a policeman. So-called because white cockatoos when raiding paddocks of grain—which they do in flocks of hundreds— post some of their numbers on trees and at the approach of human beings these warn the flock, which immediately takes flight.

passed to the customers grouped outside in the street. Finally the bottled beer gave out too and then the demand changed to wine, and then rum, and gin, until soon there was nothing stronger in the place than a bottle of lemonade. Even a bottle of crème-de-menthe which looked as though it had stood on the shelf for years was sold to an old chap – a regular customer and confirmed rum drinker.

What struck me forcibly was that men, usually so particular about their drinks in the bar, were prepared to drink anything at all. Some would hold up a note to the useful and say: 'Ferchrissake! Give's anything s'long as it's got a kick in it.'

At last the Missus told the useful to bolt the door, saying that we had sold out of everything. She had been careful, however, to save one nine-gallon keg for Monday morning, pending the arrival of the brewery waggon.

So much for Election Day! It was a good day for the publican. But despite my hopes I received no extra money on pay day. When I mentioned it later to the maid she said the union officials were in the pocket of the publicans.

After going along to vote I went out to Mrs Platt's to collect the children.

Mrs Platt opened the door to my knock, but from the expression on her face it was evident she had not expected me so early. She was plainly ill at ease as I entered and walked through to the kitchen ahead of her. I expected to be greeted by my two children, but what I saw was a different sight. Mr Platt, a little inoffensive man, was sitting at the table with two other men and women. On the table were a few bottles of beer and several glasses, and the room was thick with tobacco smoke. In one corner a tinny gramophone was scratchily rendering a Charleston number. One of the women was studying a racing guide, at the same time doing the draw-back and allowing the smoke to curl up and around her face. None paid any attention to me with the exception of Mr Platt who looked up and said 'Hullo' as I came to the doorway. I turned to Mrs Platt, who was standing beside me.

'Where are the children?' I asked.

Without speaking she indicated the ceiling with her thumb. I climbed the narrow stairs and entered the little back room over the kitchen. It was almost dark in there, although the sun was shining brightly outside. I switched on the light, and there were my two babies, sitting on the floor with their backs against the wall. Terry had one arm around Ann, whose head rested on his shoulder. When they saw who it was they started to get up, but I ran over to them and knelt down, hugging them as they clung to me. I could feel the heat of Ann's little body, and knew she was ill.

It appeared that Mrs Platt had sent her own children to the pictures. She wanted to have her session with her friends downstairs and had put my children out of the way. I might have known. The dirty cheat!

Hurriedly I went downstairs with the children, and as we reached the foot of the stairs Mrs Platt came out of the kitchen.

'Are yer takin' 'em 'ome?' she demanded.

'Yes, and I'm not bringing them back,' I said, fighting to keep myself calm.

'Oh, so that's it? My 'ome ain't good enough for yer any more?' she said sarcastically.

'That's right,' I answered. 'As a matter of fact, it isn't.'

This, it seemed, was the wrong thing to say, for she leered into my face, and said: 'Why, I've got a good mind ter job yer.'

I advised her not to do anything of the sort, and she went on to hurl abuse at me.

''oo the bloody 'ell d'yer think *you* are, eh? Why, yer only a bloody barmaid!'

As I moved the children towards the front door she followed threateningly. One of the females from the kitchen called: 'Why don't yer knock 'er bloody block off, Mil?'

By this time I had the front door open. I was worried now, for she had her mob outside in the kitchen and they were half drunk. With the baby in my arms, and a terrified little boy holding my skirt, I got out on to the footpath thankfully.

She followed me out: 'Wot about payin' yer kids' board, eh?'

'You know quite well I don't owe you a penny.'

'Yer a liar,' she flung back, 'and as far as *I'm* concerned yer can take yer bastards away from 'ere. They're only a bloody nuisance, any'ow!'

Just then a woman standing on a verandah across the street called out: 'At it again, Mil? No doubt about yer!'

This spurred Mrs Platt to greater efforts. Ignoring the woman she went on loudly: 'Anyway, where's yer old man? I wouldn't mind bettin' yer never 'ad one!'

Mr Platt appeared at this stage, and tried to pacify his bellowing wife. 'Now then, Mil, ye'll only go makin' yerself crook again.' He made an effort to get his scrawny arm around her great girth.

'Well,' she sniffed in an injured voice, 'I'm not goin' ter stand 'ere an' let 'er say wot she likes ter me!'

'Come in and 'ave a drink then, Mil,' he said, and she went inside with a parting broadside delivered over her meaty shoulder.

'Yer know wot you are? Well, I'll tell yer – yer're a broken-down toff, that's wot you are.'

I moved down the street thinking that was better than never being anything at all. Heads had popped out of windows here and there to hear this welcome morsel, and as I crossed the road near the woman who had called out, she said, 'Never mind, luv – it's all over now.'

She could see that I was really upset. I wasn't tough, I thought, although it was true I was becoming hardened gradually, and was beginning to hold my own a bit with people.

The woman went on: 'It's the best thing that could've happened. It's an old gag of hers gettin' kids to mind so's she can get a bit of extra money for booze and to pay off the pianola. Everyone's a wake-up to her in this street. She *always* reckons they owe her money. Yes, some of the poor cows pay up rather than have any trouble with her.'

I mumbled some kind of thanks to her and hurried along until we were out of the street. Ann sat limp in my arms, her head resting on my shoulder. That night her body seemed on fire. I gave her a dose of oil and put her to bed.

Terry and I had tea together. I questioned him about Mrs Platt. To my astonishment he wouldn't answer and I made a shrewd guess at what she had done to him. I told him he wouldn't go to her place any more. Then by questioning, I got from him, bit by bit, how Mrs Platt had beaten him and Ann, mostly by smacking their faces with her open hand, and threatening that if he were to tell me she would 'skin them both alive' the next day.

18

Next day I packed our things and moved my little family out to Mrs Norris's place, where I immediately put Ann to bed. She was still feverish, and I decided that if she got any worse I'd call a doctor.

Terry was bursting to get outside to the horse, so I put some old clothes on him and let him go. The Norris family had gone visiting for lunch, so I hadn't to worry that he might annoy them.

After tea I washed Terry and put him to bed with Ann, then went out to the kitchen to iron a frock for work. When I'd finished I had a look at Ann. She was delirious and appeared to have great difficulty in getting her breath. I knew it was time to get the doctor.

Trying to ignore the terror surging through me I raced down the street to the phone booth, leaving the two children alone in the house. It was dark and the light in the booth was out of order, so I ran to the little corner shop and bought a box of matches. I struck match after match as I turned the tattered pages back and forth in search of a local doctor's number. Finally I found one and rang to be informed by a woman's voice that the doctor was away for the week-end. When I told her it was urgent she said that another doctor would be sent. I thanked her gratefully and hurried home where I straightened things up while I waited for the doctor to arrive.

The sound of a car sent me rushing to the door and I opened it as the doctor stepped on to the verandah. Without a word he followed me in to where Ann lay.

I stood nervously while he asked me questions and began to examine her. Without looking up he asked me to fetch a spoon. I hurried out to the kitchen and got one. He used it to hold Ann's tongue back as he peered down her throat. He straightened to tell me: 'She has diphtheria, and I'm afraid she's in a bad way. At the moment she's in danger of choking. You'd better get her to the Children's Hospital right away. I'll ring through for a bed – but there isn't much hope for her, I'm afraid.'

With that he was gone. I thought I would faint.

How would I get her there? A taxi, I thought. But where would I get one at this time of night, and in this district? Then I remembered a private-hire car I'd noticed standing on an allotment beside the tiny cottage down the street.

Rushing down the street I found to my relief that it was there. I knocked on the door. It was immediately opened by the man I'd seen washing the car the day before. I explained the position and he said he'd come at once, not waiting to put on his coat.

I had great difficulty waking Terry, who had slept through it all. Lifting him on to the floor I dressed him hurriedly, and he began to rub his eyes and whimper, not understanding what it was all about. I carried him out and sat him in the car, then went back and got Ann. Wrapping her in a rug I sat and nursed her as the driver raced the car to the hospital. He certainly knew all the short-cuts, driving through what seemed miles of back lanes and streets until we came on to Parramatta Road. Another minute and we were swinging into the hospital driveway. As the car came to a standstill a nurse hurried out from the vestibule and took Ann from me and carried her inside. I followed.

A sister intercepted me and, indicating a long form standing by the office door, asked if I would wait. I sat down and watched the nurse pass from sight carrying my baby, then, remembering Terry, went out to the car, where, now very wide awake, he was examining the dashboard instruments.

The driver was good-humouredly explaining what the little clocks and things were for. I called to Terry to come with me. The driver offered to mind him. I thanked him but explained that we'd have to wait, perhaps for a long time. Then I remembered that I hadn't paid him. I opened my purse to get the money when he said: 'That's all right,' pressed the starter as he leant over to close the door and was gone before I could even thank him.

Taking Terry inside I sat him beside me on the form. He started a barrage of questions: Why were we here? What was wrong with Ann? Would they hurt her? Where was she? When I told him she was very sick he fell silent.

Presently a doctor came along and asked me to sign a paper authorizing them to operate. When he mentioned the word operate I nearly fainted, but I managed to sign the paper and he went away, walking quickly and silently down the corridor.

The anxiety of those next few hours left me numb and exhausted. Supposing she should die? I thought of my husband, and wondered what his reaction would be if he knew our baby daughter was fighting for her life. But I dismissed the thought with a shrug. I knew only too well that he wouldn't care what happened to us. He'd shown that only too clearly.

The sound of rubber-soled shoes and the swish of crisp linen disturbed my thoughts, and I looked up to a see a nurse who smiled and said: 'Your baby has come through the operation all right, Mrs Marsh.'

My relief was so great that I started to cry, releasing the agonies of the last few hours. The nurse stood beside me for a few minutes and in a very kindly manner asked if I wanted to stay a little longer. I told her I would like to, and she left us. After a while she came back and gave me a cup of tea. 'Here, drink this,' she said, 'and you'll feel much better.'

I thanked her and asked: 'How is she, Nurse?'

'She's quite comfortable now. I suggest that you go home. It's after midnight. Ring the hospital in the morning.'

As I sat sipping my tea she looked down at Terry, who had curled up on the form and gone to sleep, and said: 'Isn't he a nice little fellow?'

I smiled back at her. Most mothers like flattery of their children.

After thanking her again, I gathered Terry in my arms and left the hospital. It had been raining all evening, and there was still a slight drizzle. I found my way to Parramatta Road and walked to a tram-stop. Lights winked dispiritedly in the distance and the roadway shone like black glass. There was no sign of a tram, and I thought they might have stopped running, for it was so late. Then I noticed an old man leaning against the window of a pawnshop nearby. By the kitbag at his feet I guessed him to be a late-worker on his way home. He fumbled with matches and, as he puffed noisily at his pipe, the flare gave me a glimpse of a face, old and worn. I asked him what time the next tram came along, and he removed his pipe from his mouth to say that one would be along any minute. It seemed a long minute as I stood nursing Terry, my arms numb from holding him.

At last a rumbling sound told of an approaching tram. It jolted to a stop, and I climbed in and thankfully flopped into a seat. The old man sat opposite me and the smell from his pipe made me feel sick.

It was raining heavily when we reached Railway Square, where I got out and hurried under the shelter of the waiting shed. Very few people were about and, with the exception of a man stretched out full-length on a seat, dead to the world, we had the place to ourselves. A man in a white coat stood near the waiting shed, a steaming urn beside him bearing a sign 'Hot Roasted Peanuts'.

After a short wait our tram came along – an all-nighter. There is something unearthly about riding in an all-nighter travelling through a sleeping city, the whirring of the tram's

motors and the grinding of steel on steel magnified tenfold by
the empty streets; the sleepy lifelessness of its passengers; the
careless detachment of the guard; the apparent recklessness of
the driver up front cheerfully clattering past stop after stop
without pause. One could imagine him welcoming this break
from the daily monotony of stopping at every red post and
waiting patiently for the bell to be on his way again.

When we arrived home I found the light still burning in the
room, forgotten in my hurried departure a few hours before.
The bedclothes were in an untidy heap and in the pillow was
the dent where Ann's little head had rested a short time before.
I lay down beside Terry and cried into the darkness. I felt I
didn't have the guts to shoulder the burden of working and
caring for the children. Oh, how I needed a strong arm to lean
on! But there was no one I could turn to. No rich uncle or
aunt. I was on the outer.

19

Next morning, I went to the phone booth and first rang the
hospital. Standing on tip-toes I heard a voice say: 'Children's
Hospital.' I asked how Ann Marsh was. After a few minutes'
wait I was told that her condition was satisfactory, and I
sighed with relief as I replaced the receiver.

Not feeling fit for work, I then rang Mrs Smith. While
waiting for her to come to the phone I looked down at the
floor and noticed a lot of dead matches scattered about. I
thought idly that some untidy person had been in there, then
realized it had been me who had dropped them there the
night before.

Mrs Smith was very nice when I explained. 'Come in
when everything's all right again,' she said.

As I walked back home an old Irish woman standing at her
front gate said 'Hullo' to me. I had spoken to her several
times in the little corner shop, but had not known she lived
so close to me. I stopped, glad of the chance to talk to someone.
She told me she was on her way to Mass, and I told her about
Ann being in hospital. She became interested when I told her
of my having to take the children away from Mrs Platt.

'Well, it's off I'll have to be, or I'll be late for Mass. But come in and see me this afternoon and I might be able to help you, sure.'

I promised I'd visit her that afternoon and I felt somehow that I'd gained a good friend. It made me feel better. When I entered our room I found Terry sitting down trying to tie his shoelaces. Seeing me, he jumped up gleefully and cried: 'Look, Mummy, I've put my own shoes on!'

I laughed as I saw he had put them on the wrong feet. While I changed them over I told him we were going to visit a nice old lady that afternoon. The Norris family didn't seem very interested about Ann. No doubt they considered it my worry, not theirs.

I raised the knocker on Mrs Sweeney's front door and tapped gently. I heard the footsteps down the hall, the door opened and my new friend appeared. After greeting us she invited Terry and me inside. I shepherded Terry ahead of me into the cosy little cottage. I noticed how scrupulously clean the place was. Terry immediately became interested in a model sailing-ship standing on the mantelpiece.

After asking after Ann, Mrs Sweeney asked me in as many words to tell her my troubles – one could not help but confide in this dear old lady. I told her how Mrs Platt had treated the children and she cried: 'Glory be to God – what vileness there is in the world, to be sure.'

I told her about my father – how he, too, had been Irish. After telling her that the first pair of boots he had ever owned had been bought from selling papers at the Quay, she told some of her own early experiences with tales of County Clare, her birthplace.

In the midst of it, she rose, saying: 'Well, I must be after makin' a cup of tay.' Her reminiscing of Ireland brought out her nearly forgotten brogue.

She went out to the kitchen to put the kettle on. She returned presently with a teapot complete with cosy, and a plate piled high with fresh scones and cakes. Bending down to Terry, she said: 'And what'll ye be havin', Tirrince, me bhoy?'

Terry said he'd like a cake.

When we'd finished afternoon tea, Mrs Sweeney showed us the backyard where she and I sat on an old garden seat set out in the centre of the well-kept lawn. Canaries whistled in a cage hanging on the wall near the kitchen door. A little, curly-haired dog came bounding out of his kennel and made several mock-savage passes at Terry, who gleefully joined in the fun.

As we sat and talked, watching the antics of Terry and the dog, I thought how restful it was there, and thought of the Norris's home next door. I felt I never wanted to leave.

Mrs Sweeney broke into my thoughts: 'Well, I'll be off to Ireland early next year – to me son over there, but if ye like, in the meantime, I'll look after young Tirrince here, and the little one when she comes out of the hospital.'

'That's awfully kind of you, Mrs Sweeney,' I said, the words inadequate to express how grateful I was. I knew my babies would get nothing but love and kindness in that home, and it meant that I wouldn't have to lose any more time off at work – not for a while, at any rate.

So it was arranged. I was to take Terry in to her in the morning, and collect him on my return from work each night. It was marvellous, I thought. I'd never expected such good luck! I arranged to pay Mrs Sweeney a pound a week to mind the children, but it was I who did the talking. I'm sure she was not interested in the money, but was just doing it to help me.

Next morning I took Terry into Mrs Sweeney, but it was a very quiet and subdued little boy who held firmly to my hand as we walked on to her verandah. Mrs Sweeney was busy sweeping her front step and on seeing me approach smiled her greeting.

'And how is Tirrince, this foine marnin'?'

But Terry was crying a little, and clinging close to me.

'Sure an' it's not cryin' ye are, bedad?' she exclaimed.

Whereupon Terry bawled lustily.

I said something about being late for work, and Mrs Sweeney nodded as she caught hold of him firmly but gently as I forced him to let go my dress to which he had fastened with both hands, and then nodded again for me to go as she carried him inside.

Without looking back I walked quickly up the street.

The bar was empty of customers when I arrived, and Mrs Smith asked sympathetically about Ann as I prepared to start work.

I filled in time straightening up the bottles along the shelves until several men came in and ordered beers. They left after one round and had no sooner gone than the brewery waggon pulled up outside. I went to look for the useful whose job it was to help unload the barrels. The useful, a most unpleasant person at the best of times, had lost heavily on the races the previous race-day and was in an ugly mood when I found him washing bottles at the laundry tubs. As I came near him he whirled around to face me.

'The brewery man is waiting for you to unlock the cellar,' I said.

'Is 'e? Well, wot am I supposed to do about that, break out in a rash or somethin'?'

'I don't know about that, but someone has to do it.'

'Well, why doesn't the Missus do a bit for a change, the big fat slob,' he spat viciously, giving me a dirty look.

'I don't know, I'm sure. Why not ask her and find out?'

He turned and, wiping his hands on his apron, followed me across the yard mumbling something about on'y 'avin' one pair of hands.

'Cheer up!' I said. 'I'll tell you a good thing for Saturday.'

'Bah! Don't talk races ter me any more. I'm off 'em for life.'

'But this one can't get beat,' I told him.

When we reached the bar, I began wrapping bottles as the useful disappeared through the trapdoor into the depths of the cellar.

When the beer was unloaded both the brewery man and the useful breasted the bar for their usual pint on the house. The useful was, by this time, in a better frame of mind, and asked: 'Wot's the good thing for Saturday?'

'I thought you were off them for life?'

'Aw, a man's got ter try and get some of 'is money back.'

The brewery man spoke up: 'Meself, I never touch 'em. This is my hobby.' He fingered his pint lovingly and ran his tongue around his mouth. 'It'll do me; always git my money's worth.'

The useful agreed, saying: 'I believe yer right there, mate.'

'Too right I am.' The driver patted his stomach contentedly. 'The first today,' he gave a belch.

As it was only nine o'clock, I said: 'I should think so!'

It was the practice of nearly every pub to give the driver of the brewery waggon a pint on the house whenever he made his delivery, and it has always been a mystery to me how they ever managed to find their way back to the brewery each night – unless their horses needed no guiding.

20

I lived a queer kind of life. I've read about people having dual personalities and I think I almost began to develop one myself. I was becoming really efficient at my job; I was learning how to be popular with the customers while keeping them at a distance. I was learning to smile when they lifted their glasses to each other with the familiar toast: 'Here's to our wives and sweethearts! May they never meet!' A smile was worth a tip.

All day I coped with the problems of a public bar, always bright, always smiling – and all the time at the back of my mind I was wondering how Ann was getting on, whether Terry was happy – not that I had much to worry about there, as Mrs Sweeney was proving the eighth wonder of the world.

The day after I was first allowed to visit Ann at the hospital I was working in the bar, feeling happier than I had for some time, even though it was a sultry day and my feet felt as though they were walking on hot cinders. This was ideal weather for the trade and the bar was more crowded than was usual for that time of the day. As I passed a mirror I caught sight of the reflection of my face. It was flushed, and little beads of perspiration had formed on my forehead.

A large man, red-faced, and with a big stomach, saw me looking in the mirror and reached over the counter and grasped my wrist: 'Look here, kid,' he rasped wheezily. 'You're sweatin', ain't yer?'

'What about it?' I asked. I already had this bird wrung out as he was always pestering me to go out with him. He was a friend of the Missus.

'Why don't yer let me take yer out of 'ere?' he asked.

'What?' I exclaimed, with mock surprise.

'Yeah,' he continued, 'let me put you in a nice little flat somewhere near the 'arbour, where you'll get a breath of salt-air, instead of stinkin' beer and terbaccer fumes. What d'yer say, kid?'

Looking at him innocently, my eyes wide, I said: 'But you

wouldn't have enough money for that!'

'Why, I've got tons of the bloody stuff, as the Missus here can tell yer!'

I withdrew my hand sharply from his. 'Why, you wouldn't have enough, even so.'

He looked puzzled, and asked: 'Why, what d'yer mean?'

'I mean that you haven't enough money to buy me, Mr Moneybags.'

With that I hurried away to the end of the bar, and began to serve another customer. The useful could serve that one I thought. There were limits to a barmaid's geniality.

Oh yes, you learn to cope with most things in a public bar. Drink does queer things to people. There's the man who ordinarily peaceful wants to pick a fight as soon as he gets a few in. There's the argumentative drunk who shouts everybody else down. There's the amorous one and the one who treats the barmaid as though she was scum. It took some time to get used to them all and a longer time to get hardened to them.

I never got hardened to the last kind and I remember vividly the first time I struck him. It was the rush-hour and I was serving drinks as fast as I could and a little pompous man called: 'Why the bloody hell don't you get a move on?'

I went on pulling beer, feeling myself flushing scarlet, and he added loudly: 'You'd be a damn sight quicker on a pick-up. I'll take my oath on it.'

The regulars pretended to ignore him but there was a stranger in the bar, who had been watching this little scene intently. He was tall and lean with a strong, sun-tanned face. He moved over to the little man, and said, 'Apologize to the lady.' Although his voice sounded menacingly, the words were uttered in a slow soft drawl. His accent was unmistakably that of an American.

'Wot? . . . apologize to her,' he said scornfully. 'Why, she's only a bloody barmaid.'

I had been serving a customer, ignoring the man in the hope that he would go away quietly, and looked up on hearing this remark in time to see the stranger pivot quickly, throwing a punch that knocked the little man to the floor. He was out like a light.

I looked from the floor to the stranger, his rugged face set grimly.

A man bent over the little chap on the floor, trying to revive him, then straightened, and said, 'Why don't yer pick some one yer own size?' He was about a foot shorter than the stranger, so that let him out.

Then I spotted Nugget out of the corner of my eye. Nugget was a big fellow, one of the regulars. He had been standing quietly at the other end of the bar and had watched this little scene. He gave his trousers a hitch as he sauntered around to the stranger.

Sensing trouble, I quickly grabbed all the bottles and glasses from off the counter.

I heard Nugget say: 'Come on, put up yer dooks!' The stranger did so, at the same time moving quickly to put his back to the wall. Nugget followed, throwing his large fist in an arc which caught the stranger squarely on the jaw. Nothing happened, so it must have missed full strength. They exchanged punches, while the crowd cleared well back, watching. It was obvious Nugget would not be able to knock this fellow out, so one of his mates then ran in and took a hand. Yet another followed, and so there were three of them on to this stranger. Fortunately for fair play, they got in each other's way.

The constable who had just entered to see the law observed at six o'clock, drew near, stood and watched as fascinated as the rest of the audience. I didn't blame him for not interfering, for it was a wonderful show. Nugget and the stranger were slogging it out, Nugget's two mates lying on the floor, no longer interested in anything. Suddenly Nugget turned from his opponent and tottered over to the counter, leaning against it for support, and hanging his head down between his elbows as they rested on the bar.

The stranger followed him over and said, 'Had enough?'

'Jeez, yes,' Nugget gasped.

The stranger beckoned me over to serve them, saying, 'Better give him a brandy – a double header Hennessy's please, and I'll have a beer, ma'm.'

As I set the drinks before them I took a good look at the stranger, and noticed how kind his eyes were. They had a mischievous twinkle in them even after fighting the way he had.

The crowd watched in silence. The Missus and the rest of the staff stood near the till, but no one spoke. The cop still stood at the door in silence. Somebody moved over and helped one of the fellows on the floor to his feet; the other managed to get up unassisted.

The stranger finished his beer, then without a word, slapped Nugget on the back and walked out of the bar.

The silence exploded as someone said, 'Well, by gawd, wot do you know about that? A goddam Yank!'

The spell broken, everyone started talking at once. . . . That stranger was talked about for many a day after that.

It used to get busy in the bar about four in the afternoon during week days and the bar would be lined six deep. From then until six the work would be terrific. At six o'clock the useful would take off his apron, jump the counter and go along closing and bolting the doors – all but one, over which he would stand guard as the customers filed out – or were thrown out, according to how much fire-water each had managed to stow away before the call: 'Time, Gents, Please!'

It would seem that everyone thought he had a priority on the service during the last half hour, when the drinkers would excitedly raise a clamour for fear they might miss out on the last drink. I remember one old chap calling out to be served, asking for four glasses. I served him, thinking that he had three mates, but I was mistaken. He gulped one down as soon as I set them before him, and when I returned with his change another had gone the same way, and he had the other two lined up on the counter in front of him, a piggish look on his face. He belonged to a particular type which can be found in all pubs.

It is the working man who spends the most on beer, and the fuller he gets, the more reckless he becomes wanting to shout for those around him, and not forgetting to tip the barmaid who serves him.

This popular Australian custom of shouting is naturally enough the cause of excessive drinking and also is a drain on a man's pocket. I often wondered what the genial shouter's wife would think if she saw him.

I once saw a man who drank so much that he vomited where he stood. As soon as the spasm had passed he called for another, then another, much to my disgust, but I had no alternative but to serve him.

I was to find that the occurrence I'd found so shocking my first day – a man urinating where he stood rather than lose his place at the bar, was not an uncommon one. With too many men, when the drink's in, ordinary decency is out!

This last half hour was when tips sometimes fell thick and fast, particularly if it was pay-night. Then men would struggle to reach through the crowd to the counter, holding an extra coin conspicuously in their hands and shouting for service. They usually got an extra beer or two – but they certainly paid for it!

Nearly every day Ted, the S.P. bookie, dropped in, and waiting till I was free asked for a pony, his usual order. I had noticed he never drank anything else, and the pony was the smallest beer sold. He usually drank for business reasons only and the Missus began to twit him – with heavy sarcasm – about his excessive drinking.

Saturday afternoons he spent in the bar from just after lunchtime. Smith's bar was his betting headquarters. He was a popular bookie – nothing of the welsher about Ted. I often thought how easy it would have been for a police spy to give him away. He was always the best-dressed man in the bar, wearing expensive and well-cut clothes and beautiful crêpe-de-chine shirts. With a mob of punters around him, it would have been simple for a stranger to walk into the bar and point to the bookie.

Ted employed a runner – a sharp-faced little man, fitted for the part, with a bright blazer and white sandshoes. It was his job to stand by Ted until given the signal. He would then move up close and take the betting slips from Ted furtively and disappear to a place of safety until after the race result was known. Just a precaution, should a raid be made by the police on the bar, to prevent Ted from being caught with the slips on him. But Ted was never caught.

21

Every pay-night brought with it a headache as I struggled to work out my budget. I was getting a wage set by law as being adequate for one person, whereas I had two children as well. There was a pound each week to be found for my rent at Norris's, a pound to Mrs Sweeney, fares and other incidentals, the children's breakfast to be thought of each day, as well as my meals. I made a few shillings in tips each week, but these varied so much it was difficult to budget on them. Still, they helped.

The weeks went by, and then I was to go and collect Ann at

the hospital. I took an afternoon off from work and could scarcely control myself as I walked into the vestibule of the hospital and told the girl at the office window that I had come for Ann Marsh. An impatient few minutes' wait, then a nurse came along carrying Ann.

She seemed shy as the nurse smilingly handed her over to me and I said: 'Have you forgotten your Mummy, darling?'

I told her we were going home to Terry, and she began to show some interest. I knew then she had not forgotten us.

On the way home in the tram I told her all about the puppy-dog at Mrs Sweeney's place, and that Terry was having a lovely time. I told her it was lovely having my little baby with me again. As I sat hugging her, some of the passengers sitting opposite abandoned their morose broodings into space and smiled at my chatter.

When we arrived at Mrs Sweeney's I stood Ann on the floor. Terry walked over to kiss her and she almost toppled over. I caught her up in my arms. She was still weak from her illness and I told myself that I would have to be very careful with her until she grew stronger.

Like everyone else, Mrs Sweeney made quite a bit of fuss about Ann – not that Terry suffered by it, for she treated them both equally, and wonderfully well.

That night Josie came to see me, and as I sat down with her on the edge of the bed, I noticed she looked very pale, and had dark circles under her eyes. I remarked that she did not look the best, and she replied that she was all right, just a little off-colour. She lit a cigarette and puffed nervously on it. Suddenly she started to shiver violently, and her teeth chattered. Her hand trembled as she ashed her cigarette.

'Why, Josie, you *are* sick,' I exclaimed.

She nodded and asked me where the bathroom was. I hurriedly rose and took her out to the lavatory down the hall, where she vomited violently for a few minutes. I held her until she said she felt better, then took her back into our room. She flopped on to the bed and gasped: 'Oh, I feel awful.'

I told her she must have eaten something that didn't agree with her. She looked at me and said: 'I wish that was all I had wrong with me.'

'Why, what *is* the matter with you?' I asked.

'Well, I may as well tell you, Caddie – I went to a woman and got fixed up.'

'You what?'

'I'm pregnant, and went to a woman who fixed me up. Cost me six pounds.'

'Oh, Josie, you didn't!'

'It's true, all right,' and she laughed hysterically.

'Why, you should be in bed. You should have a doctor to you, instead of walking about like this.'

'All in good time,' she laughed again. 'You've no idea what the place was like. No lights anywhere – spooky like a morgue.'

'Was she a nurse, this woman – a trained nurse, I mean?' I asked.

'No, just a dirty old hag with filthy finger-nails.'

'Why didn't you walk out when you saw she wasn't clean?'

'Huh! It was too late then – she already had my dough. You see, I didn't get a good look at her until we got upstairs.' She shuddered. 'The place gave me the creeps. The old bitch swore at me – said I wasn't relaxing. As though I wasn't putting up with enough!' She lit another cigarette.

'Did she use an instrument, Josie?' I asked as I watched her puffing smoke everywhere.

'Yes, if you can call a piece of wire an instrument.'

'Oh, Josie!' I said, looking helplessly at her, not knowing what else to say. This was a new one on me – I had only vaguely heard about such things. Having babies was natural, but this was something different.

Josie started to cry, and all I could do was sit there and watch her pityingly. She looked up at me and said, 'I'm not crying because he left me. I've known that for a good while – about him leaving me, I mean. It's losing my baby, that's what hurts.'

'How far gone are you?'

'Four months.'

'Good heavens!' I gasped. It seemed that all I could do was gasp, but I was shocked.

Then she spoke again. 'You see, I kept putting it off, hoping he'd come back to me.'

'But how do you know he won't come back?'

'His boat came in yesterday and he wasn't on it. Didn't even sign on this trip.'

'Couldn't you find out anything from his mates?'

'They won't talk.' She stubbed her cigarette. 'Oh, I hate him for making me do this.'

'What are you going to do if –' I didn't know how to say it.

'The old hag gave me orders that as soon as everything was over I was to ring this number. It's the doctor's.' She took out a piece of paper and looked at it. 'She wouldn't write it out herself – she told me to.' She looked at me with red-rimmed eyes, swollen from crying. 'You must think me awful!'

Before I could answer she said: 'You must. Because you have two children and battle along with them. But it would be different with me. I know I told you we were married and all that, but that was because my baby was coming, and I thought he was coming back to marry me, but those things only happen in books.'

'You needn't have told me that, Josie. It's your business. And who am I to judge you, anyway?'

I offered her a warm drink, but she refused it, saying she'd better get home.

Lying there with Terry after Josie had gone I shuddered to think of all the unfortunate girls who must have lost their lives rather than face the cruel criticism and unjust treatment that would be their lot if they had an illegitimate child. Not only their reputation that suffers, but their chance of earning a decent living.

Several nights later Josie called and I was relieved to see her, for I was worried for fear anything had happened to her, and was going to visit her to see that everything was all right.

As I took her into my room, she said: 'Everything went O.K., thank heavens!'

'You're lucky, considering how dirty the old woman was.'

'Yes. The doctor came and said it was a complete miscarriage.'

'How did you get the doctor?' I asked.

'Oh, when it was over I got downstairs somehow and rang the number she gave me. When I got back to the room I nearly fainted, and had a stiff brandy. It bucked me up, and I went down and let the doctor in, without anybody in the residential being any the wiser. I was awfully afraid the landlady would hear me moaning, so I stuffed the corner of the pillow in my mouth. I didn't want the old girl to ring the police. I went to work the next day,' she finished up, as though it was quite a normal thing to do.

'You what?' I ejaculated.

'I had to – I had to have the rent, didn't I?'

Her defensive retort was almost comical.

'Oh!' I said, and could just sit and look at her.

22

One afternoon I was in the bar getting glasses out and generally preparing for the usual Saturday rush when Ted, the bookie, came in. He threw a glance at the only other customer in the bar, the old toss-pot standing in his corner of the bar sipping his eternal rum, then walked over to me smiling.

'How are you today, Caddie?' he asked.

I replied that I was well, and asked if he wanted a drink, as it was unusual for him to drink so early.

'You're in early,' I added. It was a pleasure to serve Ted.

He spun a shilling across the counter in his usual manner, and I caught it and whisked it into the till and gave him his change.

'Yes,' he smiled, 'the early bird catches the worm.' Then seriously. 'I came to see you, that's why I came so early – to talk to you on our own.'

I laughed. 'But we're not alone.'

He looked down the bar at the old toss-pot morosely staring at one of his hands as though he had just discovered it.

'Look, Caddie – all joking aside. How about knocking about with me? I'm serious.'

I laughed, 'Oh, I don't know.'

'How about letting me take you for a run one Sunday in the car?'

'Well, I'm very busy at the week-ends looking after the family.'

'Well, how about taking me to meet the old people?' he persisted, misunderstanding my reference to the family, as I had intended him to.

I merely smiled, and he asked anxiously: 'Look, you haven't got another bloke, have you?'

'No,' I said, not looking at him, and pretending to flick a fly off the counter with the towel. 'As a matter of fact, I don't want to go out with anyone.'

He looked across the top of his glass as he raised it to his mouth.

'I don't believe that! Anyway, I've got plenty of patience – I can wait!'

That night as I knocked off and left the hotel, I almost ran into Ted, who raised his hat and said goodnight.

I answered his greeting and went to walk on, but he took my arm and fell into step beside me, saying: 'What's the hurry?'

Before I could answer he had pulled me to a standstill at the corner and said: 'Now, don't tell me you have to hurry home to the family. Aw, listen, Caddie, have a heart . . . don't be in such a hurry. Look, I can't very well say what I want to here. Come and sit in my car. There it is over there.'

I started to protest but he took my arm firmly and led me to the car, which was standing at the kerb.

'I'm not going to hurt you,' he said, as he swung one door of the car open and I reluctantly got in.

He went round and slid in behind the wheel, then turned to me, resting one arm on the back of the seat. 'Look, Caddie, I love you . . . have done for a long time. I can't help it. I'm on the level – give me a chance!'

This was something new, and I didn't quite know how to handle it.

'I'm sorry, Ted. You may only think you do.'

'What's the difference? Look, Caddie, I want to be on the level with you, and if I don't tell you someone else will. I'm not proud of the fact, but I get my living S.P. betting . . . if the mugs are silly enough to throw their cash away, I might as well have it. If I don't someone else will. And I do a bit of sly-grog on the side, besides running a two-up school. But I'm prepared to give it all up and get a job . . . that is, if you'll have me.'

I didn't speak.

'Well, what about it, Caddie?' he asked.

Right then I wanted to tell him I was married and had two children, but somehow I could not manage it. It was nice sitting there, I thought, relaxing in a beautiful car, with a man who was apparently in love with me – or thought he was. It gave me a warm feeling to know that here was a man prepared to give up easy money, and to work for my sake. I thought of John, and of how shabbily he had treated me. It gave me a thrill of pleasure to think someone cared for me.

Ted broke into my thoughts: 'Go on, Caddie.'

I said I'd think it over.

'Whew, what a girl,' he said. 'Anyway, while you're thinking it over, what about letting me take you to a dance next Saturday night? It's a benefit for a sick digger.'

I laughed, and said, 'I'll think about that, too.'

Ted offered to drive me home, so off we went.

I persuaded him to drop me off at the corner of my street, as I didn't want to run the risk of Mrs Norris seeing me drive up to the door in a car, especially a Cadillac!

After talking for a few minutes Ted slipped out and came round to let me out. Placing one arm under my elbow he helped me out, and as I straightened he slipped one arm around my waist. As I looked up he kissed me on the lips.

It was nice being kissed like that, but I felt ashamed, standing there, as though I had no right to let him kiss me. Then I thought to myself, why shouldn't I? Hadn't John walked out on me? Why should I act like a foolish young girl when I had been through the mill? A married woman with two children!

I left Ted with the promise that I would go to the dance with him on the Saturday night and went into my room. For a while I sat down and rested my weary feet, thinking about him and about John. What a mess life was! There was my husband who'd had every chance life could offer him and who'd turned out a complete rotter. And here was Ted – on the outer so far as society and the law was concerned, and yet considerate of me in every way. The irony of things – the man I loved cast me and his children off without a thought. And another man I didn't care about wanted to marry me!

Next Saturday Ted drove me home after work and left me to get ready for the dance, saying he would call back for me at 8 o'clock sharp.

Standing in front of the mirror brushing my hair, I paused, the brush in mid-air, and gazed into the mirror at my reflection, feeling happy and excited. Standing there I thought of John again and remembered I felt the same way when he had first called to take me out.

Just then Josie came in to stay with the children, and as she took her customary seat on the bed, remarked: 'Well, the old hag is in a lot of bother.'

'Really!' I exclaimed.

'Yes. She operated on a young girl who died. The cops caught up with her, and she's been committed for trial.'

'It was those dirty finger-nails, I'll bet,' I said.

'Probably was.'

I shuddered as I picked up my coat, trying to put the thought of the dead young girl out of my mind. What good could it do her to spoil my first night out in ages?

23

The dance was held in a small hall at Pyrmont. On our arrival Ted introduced me to several men standing outside and then escorted me into the well-filled hall. He seemed to be well-known and well liked judging by the cheery greetings tossed to him from every direction.

After going to the cloakroom to leave my coat and powder my nose, I rejoined Ted and he guided me to where a group of people sat talking animatedly. One middle-aged woman, the centre of the gathering, was introduced by Ted as his mother. She was rather plump, with dark hair and eyes, and gave me a friendly smile revealing broken false teeth as Ted said: 'This is Caddie, Mum.'

Ted didn't take after his mother, I thought, except for his eyes.

She moved up and made room for me to sit down, and I took a seat as Ted turned away to speak to a little man with a slick brushback who had come over quickly.

Out of the corner of his mouth, he said: 'Any chance of getting a few dozen quarts? Mike Riley's having a bit of shivoo down at his place tonight.'

Ted said that he thought it could be done and told the man he would be with him in a minute. The little man spun on his heel and moved quickly over to the door.

Ted turned to me, and said: 'I have to buzz off for a while. I won't be long.' Then, turning to his mother, he said: 'Look after her for me, Mum.'

The orchestra, consisting of a piano, a violin and drums was tuning up on a raised platform at the far end of the hall. Suddenly the discordant sounds ceased, and the violinist rose and announced the first number – a foxtrot. A young man came over and asked if I cared to have it with him. I said I had already promised it to someone else, thinking it only right that Ted, as my escort, should have the first dance.

Then Ted's mother started to give me a ball-to-ball description of Teddy. Her Teddy was so good! Why, only the other day 'e gave a fella eight quid 'oo was gittin' put out of 'is 'ouse acause 'e couldn't pay 'is rent. And only ternight 'e give twenty quid fer the fella wot this dance is fer!' she said proudly.

I thought if he's so generous why doesn't he buy his mother some new false teeth and some decent clothes?

'Yes, as 'e sez 'imself,' she went on, ' 'e gets it easy, any'ow.'

The orchestra broke into a dreamy waltz as I saw Ted coming towards me, smiling and nodding that he wanted to dance.

Ted did all the talking as we danced, whispering that he loved me. 'You're the nicest girl here – look for yourself!'

I smiled, and he went on: 'Why, you're class, Caddie!'

I thought how well he danced, and then it came to me how long it had been since I was last on a dance floor. I didn't get much time or opportunity for dancing now.

Suddenly a young woman stepped out from a group of people standing at the edge of the floor, her scarlet dress catching my eye. As we passed she tapped Ted on the shoulder, but he ignored her, steering me towards the centre of the floor.

Later, when I entered the ladies' room and was standing in front of the wall-mirror, a flash of scarlet crossed the mirror, and I saw the wearer join a couple of others girls I had noticed as I came in. I could hear a whispered discussion and had the feeling that they were talking about me. I was right, too. I caught a whispered piece of advice: 'Go on Maudie – why don't you have her on about it? Have it out with her now!'

A common-looking girl chimed in: 'Yes, why don't yer?'

I turned and looked squarely at them, and the speaker gave me a look that started at my head and finished at my feet, and then Maudie came slowly towards me. A chorus of 'Gorn, Maud!' urged her on.

'Lissen,' she said, 'you keep your 'ands orf 'im! 'e's mine, see?'

'I beg your pardon?'

Without taking her eyes off my face she went on: 'You 'eard me! It's Teddy.'

I tried to sound unconcerned as I turned and resumed the powdering where I left off. 'What about Teddy?'

'Just this!' she snapped, beginning to feel sure of herself. ' 'Im an' me's been knockin' around together fer over two years!'

'What am I supposed to do about that?'

'Only one thing – lay orf 'im, that's all – see!'

'Hadn't you better see *him* about that?'

'Too right. I'll see 'im ternight – you can bet yer life on *that.*'

With that she returned to her friends, who had been watching the little interlude intently. I gathered up my puff and comb and walked towards the door.

Maudie intercepted me and grabbed my arm. 'Listen! Ask 'im 'oo set 'im up the first time 'e took on the bettin'? An' ask 'im 'oo paid 'is fine when 'e was nabbed? It was *me,* see! Wot's more,' she paused to give added weight to her revelation. 'Wot's more – 'e's me 'usband!'

'Oh,' I gasped. 'I – er – that's news to me.'

I certainly hadn't dreamt he was married.

'Aw, no weddin' bells or that – but I've been wife to 'im, an' you ain't in th' race. D'yer get me?'

I said: 'Yes, I think I do,' and hurried out of the room. I didn't doubt her story for one minute. No woman would go so far as to say such things if they weren't true, I thought, and many wouldn't admit such things if they were true. Well, this is the stone end of Ted, I told myself. As far as I was concerned, she could have him. I felt ashamed and humiliated as I made my way home alone.

On Monday morning I was busily polishing the counter when Ted walked in. He didn't greet me in the usual way but came over and stood before me. As I looked up he said: 'What was the strength of you walkin' out on me at the dance? You made a man feel a bit of a goat, didn't you?'

'What do you suppose you made me feel like?' I flared back at him.

'What do you mean?'

'You know what I mean, Ted. It was Maudie, she talked.'

'What did she say?'

As I moved around the counter polishing vigorously he followed saying: 'Come on, what did she say to you? Tell me!'

'She told me plenty . . . that you belonged to her . . . sole rights and all that sort of thing.'

'Yeah, and what else?'

'She said that when you were in trouble about betting she paid your fine and that she had helped to stand you up in the game.'

'The dirty slut,' he almost shouted.

'Nice man,' I said sarcastically.

'Listen, Caddie, it's a lot of tripe me owing her anything. It's true I did knock about with her for a while. She threw herself at me – so what was a man to do? Why, she's not in the same street as you – you're different.'

'How do you know that? Why, I might easily do the same if I loved anyone as much as she loves you; and besides, I think she has courage to stand up and fight for herself the way she did.'

'Aw, cut it out, now you're talkin' junk.'

'I don't think so.'

I had reached the end of the counter and the end of my polishing and was wishing to end this useless argument, when the brewery man put his head around the door and called: 'Brewery, Miss, where'll I put it?'

This gave me the opportunity I needed. So I said: 'Wait on and I'll fetch the useful.' With that I hurried from the bar. That, so far as I was concerned, was the last of Ted.

24

The following Sunday it rained heavily, and I was unable to take the children to the Zoo as I had planned. We spent the day in our room. Terry was soon bored at being cooped up with nothing to amuse him, but Ann was content to sit on the bed with her doll and watch his antics as I lay and read Sunday papers.

At lunch time, I went out to the kitchen and found room on the stove to cook our dinner. Mrs Norris was setting the table and yelling at her two offspring at the same time.

The days slipped into months and soon Mrs Sweeney would be going back to Ireland. Once again I was faced with the problem of finding a suitable place where I could leave the children.

After thinking things over I decided not to run the risk of meeting another Mrs Platt. I would try and find a church home for them. There were a few people in the neighbourhood who would have looked after them for me, but I knew they were poor and all had children of their own. They would be only interested in the few extra shillings attached to it.

So I decided to go and see the minister who had christened my babies in the hope that he would help me to find a suitable home for them.

That night, taking the children with me, I set out by tram for the Rectory. The night was bleak and miserable, and rain had been falling earlier in the evening.

As I pushed open the Rectory gate, a shower of raindrops sprayed us from the glistening archway of leaves overhead. Terry ran on ahead down the flagged pathway, and a maid, apparently hearing us approach, opened the door to us and ushered us into a room off the hall. Here was a cosy fire, and a sleepy cat stretched out on a rug before the hearth. My feet sank into a luxurious carpet as I crossed to a nearby chair. I sat down, with Ann on my lap, while Terry went over and stroked the cat.

The minister appeared in the doorway. He didn't enter the room – just stood there and asked why I wanted to see him. I told him briefly I was forced to work and had nowhere to leave the children. Could he advise me?

He looked at me coldly and said: 'I don't know of any place. What made you come to me?'

I replied that because he was a minister I thought he might know of a church home where I could board them. He shook his head and repeated that he didn't know of any place.

There was a finality about this last sentence. I felt it was time to go.

As we walked out he made some remark on the weather. The door closed behind us.

As we made our way to the tram stop I felt depressed. I'd thought that this man of God would surely help in some way or at least be sympathetic. The warm contact of Ann in my arms and the feel of my little son's hand in mine gave me fresh courage. I'd battle for them as long as I lived.

I decided to try the minister of the parish in which we lived. He was a kindly man and immediately offered to help me. He made inquiries at two Homes, both in the western suburbs. One was for boys, and the other for girls, and they each took only a few children. I was pleased at this, for I thought my children would get better attention and individual care in those places than in the larger institutions. There was some difficulty in placing Ann because she was so young, but the minister overcame that obstacle.

The day came for me to take them to the Homes. We went

first to the Girls' Home, where the matron, who was expecting me, took Ann from me as she signalled for me to leave quietly, and I hurried out the gate with Terry before he had a chance to hear her cry. He was beginning to feel uneasy I could see, but seemed too busy thinking to ask any questions. I felt like a criminal and nearly weakened about the whole thing – but I thought of Mrs Platt, and then of the nice lawns surrounding the buildings where I had just left Ann. I hurried off with Terry.

While I talked to the matron at the Boys' Home, sitting comfortably in her office, Terry clung silently to me. Miss Monty, whom the matron had introduced to me as her assistant, sat primly in a stiff-backed chair throughout the interview, and did not speak until it was time for me to go. Then in a deep, masculine voice, she called Terry to her: 'Terence, come here.'

Terry had no intention of leaving me. Miss Monty spoke again as I started to rise, and her voice was heavy with authority. Terry took a firmer grip of my dress and began to cry. I had to break his grip, and then Miss Monty came over and took him by the hand, bending almost double to reach him, so tall was she. Her height was accentuated by the longest neck I've ever seen on anybody.

I kissed Terry, telling him I would come and visit him every Sunday, but he pleaded with me through his tears: 'Don't leave me, Mummy!' I tried to reason with him, but Miss Monty told me I had better go. The matron watched impassively.

I hurried out, not daring to look back for fear I should weaken. I could hear Terry screaming as I walked quickly down the path and into the street, and I burst into tears myself. In the street, people turned to stare, but I was past caring.

I caught a tram, managing to get a compartment to myself. The conductor came swinging along the footboard giving a cheery little whistle and leant carelessly on a handrail. Looking at me in surprise, he asked: 'What's the matter, sister?'

I don't know why, but at that moment I thought it was wonderful to have someone to talk to. Even though he was a stranger, I told him what I had just done.

'Gawd, you look young to have a couple of kids,' he said.

When I told him where I had left Terry, he said:

'Well, you needn't worry – he'll have a good home there. I've been on this run for years and I see the kids from that

Home often. They're the picture of health, I can tell you. Those two old ladies know their job.'

His remarks made me feel better. I said: 'What about the tall one – you know, the deputy?'

'What that old lady doesn't know about kids isn't worth knowing,' he answered me.

I was still holding my fare in my hand, and when I handed it to him, he refused to take it. I insisted, but he said: 'That's all right. Put it back in your kick. If an inspector gets on tell him you only got on at the last stop.'

With that he swung away to collect a fare further along.

We were a stop before the station when he came along again. 'Now, don't forget. You needn't worry about either of these Homes. Better to see them there, seeing as you have to work, than for them to be getting about the streets with snotty noses, and scaling trams, don't you reckon?'

I said: 'I suppose so,' and alighted at the station.

He called out: 'Good luck!'

On my way home in the train, I thought how awful it was to part with my children. But time proved the conductor right. Miss Monty did show that what she didn't know about children wasn't worth worrying about. They both were very well cared for. As the Homes were not very far from each other I was able to have an hour at each every Sunday. Ann settled down wonderfully; but Terry not only played up the first day I took him there, but nearly every visiting day there would be a scene. He was always waiting for me when I arrived, but I had to do most of the talking, as he was more or less quiet and thoughtful. I used to try and brighten him up by telling him it wouldn't be long before we would have a home of our own; but he would just sit and listen. When it was time for me to go there was the usual fuss. Many a time I felt tempted to bring him away with me, but I had nowhere to take him – only back to room life with people like the Norrises.

Once the matron told me that although I paid the least for my boy, I was the most affectionate mother, and that Terry lived for visiting days. She said that she had remarked to her deputy Miss Monty about us, and compared Terry with most of the others boys, who were often reluctant to leave the playing field when their parents called to see them.

I was nearly aways close to tears myself when I left Terry and had to remind myself how lucky I was that my children

97

were well cared for and out of the Norris household and its continual arguments, where bad language was the order of the day – particularly at meal times.

I would tell myself how lucky we were – just as I told Terry, but nothing really consoled me for the regular weekly separation from my children.

25

A week after taking the children to the Homes, Mrs Sweeney sailed for Ireland and I accompanied her to the wharf at Woolloomooloo. I tried to tell her how grateful I was to her for all she had done for me, but she stopped me with simulated impatience. I leant over and kissed her, and she pulled away quickly, very embarrassed.

I laughed, and said: 'Gee, anyone would think I was poison!'

'Away wid ye, now, an' no more of your blarney,' she said, but could not hide her pleasure.

We said good-bye. She walked to the gangway, paused at the step and called: 'You'll be gettin' a letter in the marnin'.'

I looked puzzled, so she called out. 'It's in the post.'

When she reached the deck she leant over the rail, and one hand to the side of her mouth, called: 'P'raps it's thinkin' of a little bhoy who niver had a pair o' boots I was!'

My eyes were full of tears. A last wave from her and I turned to go, feeling miserable.

Her letter was waiting for me when I reached home. In it I found a money order for ten pounds, made out to me, and to it was pinned a little note. It was to say that I was never to forget my children, reminding me that sometimes mothers forgot their children once they put them in Homes. She said to never let a man come between me and my children – come what may. The old darling, I thought – as if I ever would!

The following Sunday morning I gave myself the luxury of an extra hour in bed, and was lying back reading the paper when a knock came to the door. It was Josie.

I told her to sit down and make herself comfortable. She kicked off her shoes and got up on to the foot of the bed. Drawing her legs up she spread her skirt around them and folding her arms about her knees said: 'I turned it in yesterday. I'm sick of working amongst that mangy lot of crawlers. I'm satisfied they've got legs on their bellies.'

'Oh well, I don't blame you for leaving. I didn't go much on them myself. What are you going to do?'

'I've got another job – it's on a sheep station out west.'

'But won't that be hard work for you?'

'I don't mind as long as I can save some dough. No chance of saving here in the city. If I stay there for twelve months I'll be able to save enough for some decent clothes and have a few frogskins in the bank for a rainy day.'

I asked her if she would stay and have dinner with me.

'I'd love to, but what will the landlady say?'

I replied that she couldn't say anything, as I'd bring our dinner into the bedroom. I said:

'I'll fix my suitcases for a table, and you can sit on the chair and I'll sit on the bed!'

Josie sat and read the paper while I dressed and went out to the kitchen where I found Mrs Norris bending down trying to light a fire in the stove, cursing the wood, the matches and the stove in the process. I asked her where I could find Mr Norris as I wanted to buy some vegetables.

'Yer'll find 'im in the yard, somewhere,' she said, not looking up.

I couldn't see him in the yard, so went into the shed at the foot of the yard. I found him stripping the leaves off a cauliflower. After buying a small cabbage and a few potatoes from him, I asked how much I owed at the same time fumbling in my apron pocket for my purse.

Without warning he caught hold of me, pulling me hard up against him. I could smell stale sweat from his body as I tried to wrench myself away.

'Don't be 'ard,' he pleaded. 'Give's a little kiss!'

I pushed him away saying, 'Take your dirty hands off me!' but he took no notice.

'Come on, wot about a little bit of a luv-up?' he went on.

I threatened to tell his wife, and he let me go. He sneered and said: 'Huh, she wouldn't believe ya. Anyway, wot's all the fuss about? A slice orf a cut loaf's never missed.'

'You dirty swine,' I gasped, and ran from the shed clutching the vegetables and stumbled up the yard and into the kitchen. As I rushed in, Mrs Norris looked up: 'Wot's the matter? Y'look as if yer've seen a ghost!'

99

'Your husband has just insulted me.' I was so rattled, the words were out before I knew what I was saying.

'Wot d'yer mean?" she snapped, looking startled.

'He put his arm around me and tried to kiss me!'

With that she lunged across the kitchen and flung the window open wide and called, 'Albert!' in a shrill voice.

Then she turned and threw me a vindictive glance, and said: 'I'll get ter the bottom of this! But I'm tellin' yer before I start that I don't believe yer!'

Albert appeared at the door and, without looking at me, said: 'Wot d'yer want?'

Mrs Norris jerked a thumb in my direction and said: 'This 'ere woman reckons you was makin' up to 'er!'

Mr Norris gave an uncertain laugh. 'Makin' up to 'er? Don't be funny! I wus on'y havin' a joke.'

Mrs Norris put her hands on her hips and snarled at me: 'I thought as much! I knew you was lying. It's people like you wot breaks up 'appy 'omes! Git out of my 'ouse as quick as yer can – I don' want any lyin' bitches around 'ere.'

'Good on yer, Kate!' chimed in Mr Norris, looking at me with triumph in his eyes.'

Just then Josie, hearing everything from the front room, came out and moving across the room placed an arm about my waist.

'Get out, you dirty mug!' she said, glaring at Mr Norris. 'How dare you speak to her like that?'

Mr Norris was taken aback.

'An' 'oo are you? Comin' inter my house. Git out before I 'ave yer up for trespassin'!'

'Oh, shut up, you big windbag and go and have a wash. You need it!'

We retreated to my room while the Norrises thought it over.

'I wouldn't let them bluff me,' she said, as I flung myself on the bed and howled. 'They're only scum. Forget it!'

I looked up at her admiringly, still sniffling. 'I'd no idea you could be so cheeky!'

'Cheeky!' she shrugged. 'You've got to be tough with that sort. I haven't been battling around since I was thirteen without learning how to handle that kind.'

I told her all that had happened, and of how Mrs Norris refused to believe me.

'Don't worry, she believed you, all right. But she wouldn't admit it.

'I remember when I was fifteen,' she continued, 'I was working at a flash joint overlooking the harbour, and one night the boss crept into my room. I yelled, and he went for his life!'

'What happened – did his wife believe you?' I asked.

'I didn't wait to find out. Next morning I just told her I was going and wanted my pay. She gave it to me – and I remember she gave me a piece of newspaper to wrap my things in, although I asked for a piece of brown paper – that's how lousy they were. I rolled up my togs and caught a ferry back to town to get another job. Yes,' she mused, 'I could write a book on my experiences.'

I looked at her thoughtfully. I was beginning to see Josie in a new light.

'Well, what about going out for a bite to eat? Then we can hunt around for another room.'

'All right, but where are we going to find another room? It's awfully hard.'

'Don't you believe it. You'll be able to find one anywhere now you haven't got the children to worry about.'

So we went into town and had dinner at a restaurant. Sitting there at the table, I couldn't help thinking of the scene at the Norrises, and said to Josie: 'Just fancy that dirty cur putting his hands on me like that!'

'Huh! I can't blame him after seeing that old bitch in the kitchen.'

Leaving the restaurant Josie insisted on paying the bill, saying: 'You can pay next time.'

We found a kennel at King's Cross. It had a gas-ring standing on a battered dressing-table, which also served as a dining-table. After paying a week's rent I left with Josie. I told her I would have to hurry, as I was going out to see the children, but she said:

'Don't you think I want to see them, too? I'll come out with you.'

After spending the afternoon with the children we went back to Mrs Norris's place, stopping to arrange to get picked up by the hire-car driver who had driven me to the hospital. When the car arrived we put the luggage in the back, and I got in with it while Josie got in front with the driver. As she slammed the door she looked across at the two Norrises who had come out on to the verandah. Seeing Mr Norris grinning she called out: 'I see you haven't had that wash yet!'

The grin vanished from his face. The driver laughed as he leant forward to release the hand-brake, and we drove away.

26

The fact that my room at the Cross was so far from Mrs Smith's hotel and because of Ted's presence there, too, I decided to try and get another job closer to the city. Being experienced in the bar now, I didn't expect much trouble in getting another job, and in that I was right.

I landed a job in the saloon bar of a large and well-known city hotel. The saloon was quite as large as the public bar at Mrs Smith's, and there were four other barmaids as well.

I discovered that there were class distinctions among barmaids as well as elsewhere and that saloon barmaids looked down on those who worked in the public bar. I could never understand why, but there it was.

The Missus here was a cold, hard woman, with diamonds smothering her fingers. With her you were just the staff and were not allowed to have even a drink of water in the bar. If at any time we needed a drink the manager would look after one's section of the bar while a hurried dash upstairs to the staff washroom for a drink from the dribbling tap over the wash basin was made.

At least, that is how it was supposed to be – but I was soon put wise by the old hands. Kneeling down behind the bar counter we would pour ourselves a glass of ginger-ale, or whatever we fancied. A whistled Joey from a barmaid was the danger signal. Often we wouldn't have time to finish the drink and would have to throw the rest of it down the sink. This waste added up, so the Missus was losing where she thought she was gaining, and because we knew it was forbidden we did it more often.

One day a customer from Mrs Smith's dropped in for a drink, and it wasn't long before others began to drop in to see me when they came to town. I was always glad to see them come in, for one gets attached to some customers – that is, the decent ones. Most publicans don't miss much, and a barmaid who can attract customers is of more value to him than one who doesn't, naturally.

My new boss was the sort who misses nothing. All hail-fellow-well-met on the surface and hard as nails underneath.

He looked at me with new interest when my old customers began to drop in – purely professional interest – rather like a racehorse owner looking at a new filly. Then he suggested that I should shorten my skirts still more – very short skirts were fashionable at the time – thus giving his customers something to look at while sipping their beer.

It was good for business, he said. A man likes nothing better than looking at a good form. He wasn't a sexy type, but believed in art or something like that.

He had said much the same to Vicky, one of the other barmaids. She had a lovely face and a marvellous figure, tall, and curved in the right places. She knew it, too, and would walk around the dressing-room posing before the mirror and mimicking the boss's views on art as revealed by the short skirt and the low neck.

Two of the other barmaids liked themselves a lot and were both tangled up with playboys whose mothers had plenty of dough. They went in for a bit of gold-digging. (Some of the girls who do this land a good catch, but more often than not they are dumped.) These two were no chickens, but got themselves up very well, had good figures and were made-up like movie stars. They had a flat somewhere at Double Bay, and each had a Johnny who shared her flat with her. They were much younger than the barmaids, and haunted the saloon bar dressed up to kill. They were a sort of gigolo to the barmaids. They did not appear to work anyway. They were in with the right clique, and brought them along there to drink, which was done obviously to help the girls keep their takings up. This is important in a saloon bar. If a barmaid in a saloon bar doesn't keep up the good work she is no good there. Besides, a good saloon barmaid can make a bit for herself. There are ways and means as I was to learn.

The other barmaid was Leslie, a very tall woman, blonde and willowy and rather attractive. Her age was hard to judge but I put it at about thirty-five, which may have been a little hard on her.

They all seemed extremely sophisticated to me and I was rather in awe of them. The first evening I listened to them in the dressing-room as we prepared to go home, with the sense of having stepped into another world.

As Leslie was taking her dress down from a hanger, she called: 'Where to tonight, Vicky?'

Vicky, who was bending over squeezing her foot into a shoe, looked up and winked a violet eye (the only time I've ever met violet eyes). 'Me? I'm going out with a real good sort tonight.'

'Do I know him?'

'Yep, I think so.' Vicky posed before the mirror.

'Don't tell me it's that big hunk of beef in the grey suit . . . the one you neglected all your other customers for tonight.'

Leslie stepped up beside her.

'That's the cargo!'

'By the look of him, he is just a dead lair. Anyway, where's he taking you?'

'To the Cavalier . . . dinner and dance.'

'Where the hell is that!'

'Of course you *wouldn't* know, seeing that Campbell Street is your long suit.'

'What's wrong with long soup? Anyway I'd rather have that than silly hores de erves, and asparagrass on toast. Give me a real good feed for mine.'

'And what's wrong with a porterhouse steak . . . can anyone tell me?' Vicky said tartly as she looked up without expecting a reply.

'Anyway, judging by the way he was tearin' the skee into him he'll be four sheets in the wind . . . I like my bloke to know what he's doin' when I'm out with him,' Leslie retorted.

Vicky laughed. 'That's all you know. Why, I watered it down nearly to the plimsoll line.'

She skipped to the door. As she left she called out, 'Well, so long, tarts,' and the door closed behind her.

Well, I thought, I'll have to watch my step here.

I was to find both Vicky and Leslie really good sports to work with. The other two were so wrapped up with their upper-crust boy-friends, they scarcely deigned to notice us. Leslie and I became very friendly, and she invited me up to her flat, which was also at the Cross. She told me she had a little son and that he was at college. I wondered how she could manage to pay the fees for that out of her wages, which were the same as mine. One night I met her boy-friend at her flat – a very jovial fellow I couldn't help liking. He was never without a cigar in his mouth, and I gathered he was a bookmaker.

After working with her for a while Leslie's ability to maintain her son at college was no longer a mystery to me, for in addition to her bookmaker friend I saw her work the till many times. For instance, if she made a sale to the value of ten shillings, she would ring half the amount on the cash-register, and pocket the other half. She certainly made a welter out of it. It was a cute dodge, all right. However, the business seemed as though it could stand the strain.

27

Under Leslie's training and with her constant prodding, I soon became one of the crowd – or at least I imagined I did. I was happy enough in my job and learned to hold my own with the slangy sophisticated women with whom I worked. I flattered myself that there were few traces left of the country bumpkin who had stepped off the train crowned by an atrocious scarlet hat. I had no worries about the children, though I missed them unbearably. I was going to parties quite a lot with Leslie's friends. I began to smoke and have an occasional drink.

Leslie had said, 'Go on, a little drink will do you good, and a fag will help to soothe your nerves.'

Somehow I wanted to be always on the go, hating to be alone with my thoughts. Despite myself, I still thought of John. Doubtless it was a reaction that I thought I should start to enjoy myself, although what I meant by that I would have had difficulty in explaining at the time.

I must have seemed a queer sort of mixture to the crowd for I realize now, that though I thought I was sophisticated (the fashionable word in those days) I was still really very much the inexperienced country girl John had married. And, most difficult of all to explain to anyone, particularly the men who began to show an interest in me, I still thought of myself as married to John. I'm afraid I had very old-fashioned ideas about marriage, and I was always getting shocks.

One night I was at a party at Leslie's flat.

I noticed that Leslie's boy-friend wasn't there and as she went past with a tray of drinks, I asked: 'Where's the boy-friend, Les?'

'Mind your own business,' she snapped.

The young man sitting next to me obliged with: 'I suppose he's taking his wife to the pictures.'

So men could be as catty as women, I thought.

One of the women sat down at the piano, and began to pound the keys in accompaniment to a bald-headed man, who began to render 'Sweet Adeline' in a poor voice. When he'd finished he bowed to the applause, which was enthusiastic, seeing that most of those present talked while he sang and others quite openly showed they were bored.

This was followed by a recitation, 'Not understood,' given by a young man with brushed-back hair.

That's me, I thought, 'not understood.'

I'd come to the party to try and forget, but the fire water I was consuming only tended to make me morbid. I thought of John and Esther and I believe I began to cry. I had been drinking as fast as drinks were handed to me, not caring. I'd never drunk at parties before, and didn't realize that we all have a limit – some of us very small. Finally I felt the room slowly turning over. I rested my head on the back of the chair and passed out.

I faintly remember voices and someone trying to help me. Someone said: 'She's fainted' – and someone else: 'No, she's under.'

Next morning I awoke to find myself in Leslie's bed. My head was splitting. Hardly able to keep my eyes open, I looked about me. Leslie was standing at a cheval mirror powdering her face. She'd heard me move.

'How'd you sleep, honey?' she asked.

'Oh, my head,' was all I could groan.

She laughed unsympathetically and said as she went out, 'You certainly had one over the eight last night.'

I crawled out of bed and looked around for my dress and stockings. I had my underclothes on and I struggled into my clothes. My head felt as if it would burst as I moved about.

Leslie came back into the room and I asked her why she hadn't sent me home last night.

'Gawd, that's a good one. I couldn't get you to do a dam' thing. I wanted to call a cab for you but you acted like a fool.'

'Did I?' I tried to remember. 'I'm sorry if I was troublesome.'

'Oh, that's all right. Don't let it worry you – it's past now – forget it.'

'Well, I'll see you later,' I said and went to walk out.

'You'd better fix yourself up a bit before you go,' she advised me. 'You hair looks as though the birds have been nesting in it. And look at your dress.'

'What did I say last night?' I asked, as I made an effort to make myself more presentable.

'Oh, nothing much, just that you seemed to have John on your mind – that was all.'

'Well, thanks again for looking after me, Les.'

'That's nothing, it was the least I could do for you, sweet.'

I picked up a cab outside the door. I had to ask the driver to come up to my room as I had no money with me. I closed the door. That was that! But I decided not to go to those sort of parties again and seriously to leave strong drink alone. Drink couldn't make me forget my worries.

28

Monday morning in the bar was always quiet, with very little to do except pull an occasional beer and stand around trying to look indispensable whenever the Missus came into the bar. After lunch, business would pick up, and by four o'clock we were usually too busy to look at the clock. Although the saloon bar was supposed to be more genteel than the public bar, the crowd was just as thick, and just as insistent and, nearing six o'clock, just as noisy.

Most of my customers were business and professional men about the city. A few workers chose to pay a little more to drink the same beer and spirits under almost the same conditions as those found in the public bar.

They were mostly decent fellows, but now and then I would meet a snag. One fellow in particular was a real pain in the neck. A big, jovial, fellow-me-lad this one, as big a nuisance to his drinking mates as he was to me. He was some kind of minor boss and usually drank with several of his employees, which explains why they put up with his habit of having a joke at someone else's expense.

One Friday night he was standing at the bar surrounded by his usual audience of back-slappers. He called for half a dozen beers, and a whisky and soda for himself. I placed the order before him and as I did he leant over the counter and in a whisper which could be heard by all nearby, said: 'Listen, baby, what would you charge to do the night with me?'

I was flabbergasted – but only for a second. I knew that every eye was on me. Leaning over the counter, I said in an equally loud whisper: 'You go home and find out what your wife charges – or better still, your daughters. I'll charge the same.'

There was a burst of laughter and one little fellow said: 'Well, you did ask for it.'

The look he got from his boss must have made him regret speaking. I don't think that smart alec meant what he said, but that's just the trouble.

Some men think it awfully smart to insult a woman behind a bar. I've often heard it said – particularly by those who have an interest in the liquor racket – that if a customer says anything out of place to a girl behind the bar, she must have encouraged it. That is a lot of hooey. When a man is three sheets in the wind he would be capable of insulting anyone. It depends entirely on the temperament of the drunk.

I became good at my job. I had to be. I was there to make money and I made it. If an inch off the bottom of my skirts meant an extra 5s. a week in tips, I was prepared to put up with the boss's idea of 'Art'.

Barmaids generally have a bad name. Some of them are not too nice, but most of them are decent, hard-working women, and there are plenty like me who slaved to keep their children. Some of the more fortunate ones lived with relatives, while others fared much the same as I did.

I learned to put the boss before sentiment, with a complete realization of what I was doing. It was my living. I was popular with the customers generally, with always a smile for anybody who breasted the bar. I took an interest in them, knew what they liked to drink. I treated them all the same, unlike some barmaids who rush to serve a good-looking man and pretend not to notice a working man in dirty clothes.

Above all, I never took my troubles to work. A good listener, I avoided voicing an opinion wherever possible. Some customers will tell you their troubles at the drop of a hat. Some of them tell of their domestic life – whatever happens to be troubling them. Quite seriously they asked you for your advice on all sorts of matters.

One of them (I'll call him Jacko), a tall, pale-faced man with a thick mop of hair that continually dropped on to his forehead, used to tell me about his wife who, after having seven kids in seven years, got to doing her own abortions. She swore she'd have no more kids. Each time this happened, which was often, he would come in and tell me 'She's done it again.'

I would have to sympathize, and say I hoped it wouldn't happen again, or something like that.

Then one day he came in, asked for a stiff brandy, and told me she had done it again . . . and was dead. . . . A collection was taken up for him in the bar.

He cried, his head buried in his arm, leaning on the counter. He was left with the seven kids. He was never away from the pub after that.

Some of them would ask me to suggest a suitable present for a girl-friend or wife. Some of them brought papers to me to help them fill in . . . all sorts of things. Some of them even asked me to suggest a name for their new baby.

It has often been said that a man does not go into a bar to see the barmaid. That he goes there for a drink. . . . That is all right, but once in the bar many a man falls for the girl behind the counter . . . I have seen that often. Many a married man has got himself in a jam over a barmaid. Many a drunk has told me I was his ideal woman, or something like that.

They would come in to drown their sorrows at home, caused in the first place by drink, I suppose – and would probably go home drunk and cause a bit more trouble. But I couldn't stop to worry about that. I'd have been out on my ear if I had.

I played no favourites and never gave a drink away. Lots of times I was told I was hard, but they didn't seem to mind for all that. As the boss paid my wages, I worked for him, and studied his interests as far as the business was concerned, and if the chance came to make a little extra profit, I did so. A man asking for wine or spirits, would get an inferior brand at top prices, if I judged him incapable of knowing the difference.

The customers would have been surprised to see me going around after the doors had been closed at night, filling enamel buckets from the drip-trays under the taps with the flat beer lost during the day. These buckets were left at the cellar door ready for the useful to take downstairs in readiness for next day's business.

I did my best to encourage customers to drink and stood ready to fill a glass as soon as it became empty. The customers thought this was good service, which it was, I suppose, but it was good for business too.

Spirits were not often true to label and when publicans were prosecuted for that offence, the plea usually was that the bar-maid or barman was responsible – the publican knew nothing about it. Knew nothing about what was going on in his own hotel!

When a customer appeared to be a connoisseur he would get his drinks true to label – others would get anything once they had had four or five and could not tell the difference. One could not ring the changes on a connoisseur – they don't drink enough to make them lose their taste.

I remember one occasion when I was sent into the public bar to relieve a barmaid off sick. A big wharfie came in reg-ularly at five-thirty. He always drank pints, and insisted that a dash of bottled lager be added, to give it a bite as he put it. There was always a disturbance when he was served. The boss and other members of the staff would not give him the dash of lager, for it would have been unprofitable.

I took him in hand, and always served him myself. Pulling his pint, I would hold it in one hand and lift the lager bottle up so he could see the label, and would add the dash. He'd watch the operation, then lean on the counter and gaze around the company with a smirk of triumph, saying what a good girl I was, and that the others weren't worth a cracker. He didn't know that I'd filled the lager bottle with draught beer earlier in the day in anticipation of his arrival. This was a tactful move on my part, aimed at quietening him, as his loud and heated demands could quickly lead to a disturbance in the bar – the last thing the boss wanted – or I for that matter.

No publican wants to see a brawl in his bar, naturally. It means loss of business, for a brawl takes the crowd's mind off drinking. They either stand and watch it, or take a hand in it themselves, depending on their mood. I've seen a crowded bar emptied in a matter of seconds as the crowd rushed outside to see a brawl which had transferred itself to the street.

There was no racket we didn't get up to in that pub, and yet it was one of the most popular bars in Sydney.

A health officer walked into the bar one morning and the manager showed him around, finishing up in the cellar.

After he had completed his inspection, the boss came to me and said: 'He's condemned a dozen boxes of cigarettes. Do you think you could get rid of them?'

I said I'd try.

'Shove 'em off at any price you like. I'll leave 'em to you.'

'It'll be hard to sell them cheaply. The customers'll tumble something's wrong with them.'

He rubbed his chin, 'I never thought of that.'

'I'll try and push them at their original price.'

'Anything you like, as long as you get rid of them.'

I did get rid of most of them, sorting out the best of them, and destroying those which were too mildewed to deceive anyone. No one ever complained!

29

Leslie and I used to have our lunch together, sitting in Hyde Park munching sandwiches and throwing crumbs to the pigeons. One day Leslie said she wanted to see a girl-friend who worked nearby, and asked if I would go with her. I agreed, and we walked over to a large building facing the park and went up some stairs to a small workroom. About twenty girls were sitting about on forms and stools, some by their machines, eating their lunches as we went in. Leslie walked in as though she owned the place. She was like that. Secretly I wished I could be like her – so sure of myself, and with such poise. I envied her.

I stayed near the office while Leslie went into a partitioned room at the far end of the workroom. A tall, fair man came out of the little office near where I was sitting. He was wearing a grey dustcoat, and I said to myself that this must be the boss. He was not only strikingly handsome but had an air of distinction even in his dustcoat.

He looked at me inquiringly. I felt flustered and said: 'I hope you don't mind me sitting here. I'm waiting for my girl-friend.'

He smiled and I thought he had the kindest smile I'd ever seen.

Not at all,' he said, and went back into his office as Leslie came along.

'Come on, we'll be late for work,' she fussed.

When we were on our way back to the pub I asked: 'Who's the good-looking sheik at the factory?'

'Oh, that's the boss. They tell me he's very good to his workers.'

I said it must be nice to have a good boss, and she replied: 'Yes, they all call him by his Christian name, which is a good sign.'

'Happy family sort of thing.'

'Yes, pays top wages, and never puts the hard word on them either.'

'Huh! He'll go broke,' I remarked; and asked casually, as I didn't want to appear too interested: 'What's his name?'

'They call him Peter. I can't pronounce his second name. He's Greek.'

'I've never seen a fair Greek before,' I said unbelievingly.

'Well, he is – that's all I know about it,' replied Leslie emphatically.

Then she went on: 'My girl-friend there is the forewoman. She's been trying to land him for ages.'

'What – no success?'

'No, and I don't think she's got Buckley's chance, either.'

'Why, is he married?'

'Married? No, not that I know of,' adding, 'you're very interested.'

'Oh, not particularly.' I hoped I sounded offhand.

'As a matter of fact, Joan's invited me up to her flat tonight for a game of bridge, and Peter's agreed to come along and make up a fourth,' Leslie remarked, and the subject was dropped.

But, I told myself, I *was* interested.

Next night Leslie called as I was about to get into bed. She exclaimed in surprise as she entered the room, 'Don't tell me you're going to bed! What's the matter, are you sick? It's only eight o'clock.'

'Oh, I felt down in the dumps, and thought I'd have an early night.'

'Look, I called to get you to come out. It's early. Slip some clothes on and come for a run. I've got a boy-friend and his cobber downstairs; we're going to Tom Ugly's. Come on, the run'll do you good.'

'All right. But I'm warning you – don't go ducking off and leaving me with the other bloke.'

'Cross my heart! I'll slip down to the car and tell them. Hurry up.'

I dressed and went downstairs. A large black sedan was standing at the kerb. Leslie was standing there talking to the driver. I walked over and she introduced me to him. 'Caddie, this is Joe.' And then, to the man sitting in the back, 'Tom – Caddie.'

We drove to Tom Ugly's and had a delightful meal of schnapper and oysters. Tom seemed a very nice chap – big and happy-go-lucky, and was almost gallant towards me. He didn't want to paw me, a fact I appreciated. Joe, too, behaved with equal decorum, and I thought to myself that here were two very nice chaps.

When Joe suggested we all go home to his place for a little sing-song and Leslie agreed, I raised no objection.

We arrived outside a new-looking cottage fronting a street littered with the barricades used when road-work is being carried out. I hadn't the faintest idea where we were but decided it must be one of the new suburbs. Joe led the way inside. The lounge was nicely furnished. A piano stood in one corner, and Tom made straight for it. Joe and Leslie went out – to the kitchen to make coffee, they said, as they left the room.

I sat down on the lounge as Tom started to play a lively jazz tune, relaxing and watching him sway to the rhythm as he played.

That Leslie had left me, in spite of her promise, didn't worry me. I thought idly that if it was Joe's place there were plenty of signs of a woman's touch about the room. It was a large cottage – no bachelor apartment – so where was the rest of the family?

I began to feel uneasy as time slipped by and Leslie and Joe still stayed in the kitchen – or wherever they were. All sorts of things were running through my mind, when I heard the sound of a car outside and the sound of the front door closing. A big woman strode into the room, glanced swiftly at me, and without a word, went quickly out towards the back of the house.

Tom played serenely on, unaware of the new arrival.

Through the noise of the playing I heard a series of bumps and the sound of voices raised in anger. Tom kept right on playing. I'm sure he heard nothing.

By now I was getting frightened. There was something definitely wrong with the set-up. I grabbed my coat from the back of the chair and fled quietly out the front door, stumbling over heaps of paving material and splashing through the darkness until I reached a main road. A tram was coming towards me, and I made a dash and caught it. Several stops further along the conductor came for my fare, and I found that the tram was heading away from the city. I got out and waited for one going the other way.

Once in the city I breathed a sigh of relief. I had feared that someone might follow me from that house. All the stories I had heard about white-slavers and opium dens ran through my mind.

Safely in bed I laughed at my fears, but thanked my lucky stars all the same. Leslie certainly knew more than she pretended, and Joe was certainly not her boy-friend – not the one I'd met, anyway. Whatever she'd got from the big woman served her right, I told myself, and fell asleep.

The next day when Leslie came into the bar she giggled. I said: 'You're a beaut.'

'What did you clear out for?' she asked.

'There was something fishy about that place. Who was that woman who barged in?'

'That was the notorious Sadie Power, in person,' said Leslie, still giggling.

'What!' I was astounded. 'D'you mean to tell me you knew it was her place?'

'Yes, but I didn't expect her to turn up. She's Joe's wife. Gawd it was funny. She dived straight at me, and swung a punch. I ducked, and Joe dropped her cold. When she came to, they squared off to each other, and I served the coffee and sandwiches in the lounge. Everything finished up all right.'

'Then who was Tom?' I asked her.

'He's a big-shot in the dope business.'

'Whew,' I gasped. I had been amongst notorious underworld characters and hadn't known it.

'Leslie,' I said sternly, 'that's the last time I'll go out with you.'

I couldn't help laughing to myself through the day as I thought of that night out. Leslie was certainly a hard head, all right, but I liked her – she was straight as a die. She had had a hard life, and had taken life as she found it. I couldn't blame her for that. Once I confided to her that I still loved John. She said:

'Don't be a bloody fool! He did the dirty on you, didn't he? Then go out and have a good time. You know the old saying – the best way to forget one man is in the arms of another.'

Easier said than done, I thought. I'd not met a man who had made me want to forget John that way.

30

A couple of days later I was flat-out pulling beer in the evening rush when a voice said quietly: 'When you're not busy.'

I straightened up and found Peter leaning over the counter, smiling. 'Oh, hullo,' I said, trying to sound casual, though my heart missed a beat. 'What brings you around these parts?'

'You, of course.'

'Me?' I was as surprised as I sounded.

He smiled and nodded, then said: 'I'll have a shandy, please.'

I set his drink before him, and trying to keep the excitement out of my voice, called out to Leslie: 'Look who's here!'

Leslie came down to us and asked: 'What's the game, big boy?' then darted back to her customers, calling back: 'I'll see you later.'

I was too busy to stop and talk to him, and he stood in the saloon right up till six o'clock. I noticed how nicely dressed he was and how very good-looking. His accent was charming. When the cry came from the public bar: 'All out, gents, please,' Peter came over and said: 'If you don't mind, I'll wait outside for you.'

Of course I didn't mind, but didn't say so. Instead, I nodded offhandedly, and he went out of the door leaving his unfinished drink on the counter.

Thrilled at the prospect of meeting him I hurried through the cleaning up in half the usual time and rushed upstairs to change.

Leslie came in right behind me and said: 'You're a fox.'

'Why, Les?' I asked pretending I didn't know what she was driving at.

'You know quite well what I mean. Now I know why you were so anxious to get Peter's pedigree from me the other day; and kidding you were not interested.'

'That's the only time I've seen him, Les, fair-dinkum.'

Leslie showed her disbelief.

'And now I think of it he was asking questions about you the night we played bridge. But he was so casual that I didn't think he was interested.'

I felt thrilled, but didn't say anything. I didn't want Leslie to know just how happy I was that after only a brief look at me Peter was as interested as I was. At least I hoped he was.

To sidetrack the conversation, I bent to straighten the seams of my stockings and caught my nail in one, causing it to ladder. 'Oh, blow you, Les, now see what you made me go and do. And they're the only decent pair I possess,' I moaned.

'Come on, give me a bit of that mirror,' she said, moving over near me, and surveying herself critically, she began powdering her nose.

'Oh, well, I'd better be off now,' I said as I picked up my coat and bag. 'See you tomorrow.'

Peter was standing near a small car by the kerb, and as I walked towards him, he tossed his cigarette into the gutter and opened the car door for me. He slid in behind the wheel and started the motor, and offered me a cigarette from a gold cigarette case. I said I didn't smoke and he asked if I minded him smoking. I said no, of course not, and he lit a cigarette and slipped the case back into his pocket. Then he swung the car expertly into the stream of traffic, flicking the wheel about with one hand. He asked where I lived, and then headed the car up William Street, and soon we were where I lived. It was only a little way from the bright lights of King's Cross but the stream of traffic flowing noisily past the end of the street contrasted with the gloomy quiet of the tenement I now called home.

He seemed bent on getting me to talk about myself. However, I managed to steer the conversation away from my affairs. He told me something of his own life. He was a Greek, and had lived for several years in the United States. That accounted for his unusual accent, I decided. He had no relations in Australia.

Peter let me out at my front gate, and asked if I would meet him next evening for dinner. I said yes, thinking I could do with a good feed. It would help me balance my budget. He said goodnight and drove off.

I went inside and changed from my street clothes before cooking myself an egg on the gas-ring. Then I got out my old black frock and pressed it ready for the next evening, and cleaned my black patent-leather shoes. The heels were worn down. I'd have to drop them into a bootmaker on my way to work. I wanted to look as nice as possible, for I knew Peter would be immaculate.

It was high time, I told myself, that I bought myself some new clothes. But with ten shillings each for the children, new clothes to buy them and fifteen shillings room-rent to find, to say nothing of the food and other incidentals I had to budget for, I wasn't left with much to spend. I had a shower and brushed my hair, then tried to manicure my nails – a rather hopeless proposition, as they were soft and cracked from the continual sloppings of beer.

Sitting there on the bed I thought how nice it was to have someone taking an interest in me. Then I thought of John and wondered what he would think if he saw me with Peter. Of course, I told myself, he wouldn't be jealous, but I bet he'd get a shock seeing me with a man like Peter. Reminiscing, I thought how much better-looking Peter was, although I didn't go much on good-looking men as a rule, preferring the rugged type. But I was flattered to think Peter should choose me.

Well, I had my first dinner date with Peter – the first of many. The next Sunday we were sitting in his car in the Domain, looking out on the warships lying around Garden Island. Tiny ferries were foaming their way carefully through shoals of sailing craft which seem to appear on the faintest promise of a sunny week-end.

It was while sitting there that Peter told me he was married and that his wife was in Athens. She had refused to join him in Australia. He also told me that they had been married when very young by family arrangement.

I laughed nervously and said: 'I've a past, too Peter – I've been through the mill.'

He replied that he didn't care what mill I'd been through. 'Of course,' he went on, 'I'd be happier if you'd not been through the . . . er . . . what you call it? . . . mill. But now it makes no difference to me. Why should it?'

'Well, you see, Peter . . . I'm married, too, and have two small children.'

I went on to tell him about John and how I had come to leave him. Peter sat and listened and when I finished he said. 'I'm not going to pretend that I'm not surprised and that what you've just told me doesn' hurt. I can only say how sorry I am not to be the father of your children, because I love you.'

He told me he would write to his wife asking her to divorce him – and asked me about getting my divorce. He wanted to know all about the children, and when I told him where they were, he asked me if he might drive me out to see them. As they were mine, he *must* see them.

When I told him I was going out to see them that afternoon, he asked could he go out with me. I found it difficult to explain, but I wanted to see the children alone before introducing them to Mummy's new friend.

However, I promised him that I'd take him to see them soon.

Peter kept me up to my promise, and the next Sunday we drove out to see the children. We called first for Terry. I left Peter in the car while I went in and saw the matron. She gave me permission to take him over to see his sister in the car, provided I had him back before four. Miss Monty went out and called Terry and he came running. I bent down and kissed him, then led him out to Peter. I'd already prepared him for this meeting with Mummy's nice friend.

I slid into the front seat beside Peter, and drew him on to my lap. 'Peter,' I said, 'this is Terry.'

Peter said: 'Hullo, Terry. How are you?'

Terry replied that he was very well, thank you. I was pleased to see how well-mannered he was. That conductor was certainly right about Miss Monty.

The two men talked as we drove along the highway to see Ann. I just sat and listened. There was nothing forced about Peter, I decided. He was genuinely interested in Terry. Deep down I was worried, for all that. I recalled John's threat about taking the children from me, and my ignorance of the law didn't help to make me any easier in mind. I was afraid Peter might somehow upset the picture and I would lose the children. Ann was a little shy as I introduced her to Peter, but this was to be expected from a little girl, I thought.

Peter and I sat on a garden seat set on the lawn in front of the main building watching Ann explaining the intricacies of hop-scotch to Terry. He remarked on how healthy they both looked. Ann obviously was his favourite. Presently he went out the gate to the car. He was back in a few minutes with a large parcel. I watched as he unwrapped it, wondering what was coming. He lifted the lid of a cardboard box to reveal a large doll.

Ann came over slowly, not taking her eyes off the beautiful

thing and stood staring as though afraid to touch it. I handed it to her, saying: 'Isn't it lovely? You must thank Peter for it.'

She managed to drag her eyes away from it long enough to say, 'Thank you, Peter.'

She took the doll and sat down on the grass.

Peter had been busy opening the rest of the parcel, and now drew forth another box, which he handed to Terry, who thanked him and then took the lid off. His eyes popped when he saw a set of trains. Then he sat down next to Ann and they compared notes.

I gave them a bar of chocolate each, telling them to hand them in to their respective matrons. It was a rigid rule at both places that all sweets must be handed in – a rule, it had been explained to me, to prevent thoughtless parents making their children sick.

Driving back to the city after delivering Terry, Peter remarked on how well-mannered they both were. I could see he was impressed.

When we reached my place I said: 'I'm sorry I can't ask you up to my room for a cup of coffee – my highly-respectable landlady would have a fit if I took a man into my room.'

He looked at me steadily.

'How about coming up to my flat sometime? If you like I'll leave the door wide open.'

31

The months passed and my friendship with Peter deepened. I was happier than I had been since the first year of my marriage. Peter took me into a new world – a world of which I was the centre. It was a new experience for me and a very pleasant one. I went to Peter's flat – another new experience. I hadn't realized till then that people lived in such quietly elegant ways, taking for granted things I'd read about only in books. My mother-in-law's house suddenly shrank to its proper proportions and her so-called entertaining seemed very stuffy and unsophisticated.

Peter had a bachelor flat, furnished comfortably and in good taste. He told me he owned the furniture and linen. He was the perfect host, insisting on my sitting down in the lounge while he went to the kitchen to prepare supper on my first visit. Alone with my thoughts I recalled John saying how I had bored him and how he had detested me. I thought then of Peter, and it gave me some satisfaction to know that with him, at least, I had influence. I wondered what John would have said.

I had nicknamed Peter 'Valentino', because he was beautifully built. He called me 'Chèrie' and 'Angel'.

That was a wonderful summer.

My friendship with Peter gave me a new confidence in myself. I began to feel really that the little girl from the railway-camp had gone forever; there were so few traces of her and just a few of the girl John had first dazzled and then bullied. But you can't throw off your past as easily as that, as I found. Leslie was always urging me to 'go the whole hog'.

'It may seem good tactics to keep Peter dangling, but someone else will snap him up if you're not careful,' she used to warn me, and to my murmured doubts about John, she would cry again: 'The best way to forget one man is in the arms of another.'

She was right, I found eventually. But it wasn't as easy as all that for me. If Peter and I had been free to marry, I'd have married him like a shot. But to take a lover – it wasn't 'tactics' on my part, far from it. If Peter had been more insistent it might have happened earlier. But he let me take my own time.

'I want you as my wife,' he used to say each time I hung back. 'I cannot marry you yet but when you come to me you will be my wife as truly as if we were married in the cathedral.'

Strangely enough, for all my experience of John, I never doubted him. There was something about Peter that made you trust him utterly.

When at last one evening I stayed with him, it all happened so easily and naturally that I wondered afterwards what all the dilly-dallying had been about.

I hadn't known that love could be like this. So tender as well as so passionate – so full of thought for me as well as for him. Indeed I came to realize that until I knew Peter, I hadn't known what love was at all.

When I awakened in the morning, for a moment I wondered where I was. I could hear Peter moving about in the kitchen, and the appetizing aroma of sizzling bacon came into the room. Snuggling under the covers I thought how fine it felt to lie between lovely sheets, which bore Peter's monogram embroidered on the corners. This was luxurious. My nerves had taken a holiday.

The enticing smell from the kitchen finally proved too much for me. I got out of bed and slipped into Peter's dressing-gown. It was miles too big for me, so I turned back the cuffs. Pushing my feet into his slippers I flip-flopped out to the kitchen.

'Good morning, darling,' I said, and he turned and took me in his arms.

'Good morning, Angel, did you sleep well?' he asked after he had kissed me.

'Yes, darling – and I'm very hungry,' I said, sniffing inelegantly at the bacon. 'My, but it smells good.'

I watched Peter set out the breakfast.

I felt bubbling with happiness – the first time for many weary years.

'I couldn't dream of letting you go away from me, Peter,' I said mock-seriously; 'you're such a good cook!'

'What! Not because you love me?' he replied with assumed indignation. Then he took me in his arms, lifted me off the floor and kissed me very gently.

I experienced such a rush of emotion – sheer happiness at his deep affection that I nearly cried. It showed me how hungry I was for love.

When he put me down, I reached up and gave him a kiss. 'Enough of this,' I said. 'I'm starving.'

I picked up a plate of toast from the stove and followed him out on to the little balcony where he had set the table. From where we were sitting Peter was able to point out the various landmarks of the harbour, the bays and headlands. A ferry moved slowly across the water to Clifton Gardens. Beyond it we could pick out the cars on the vehicular ferry gliding across to the North Shore, a sight long since faded from the Sydney scene.

A few sailing craft were setting out on the promise of what seemed a beautiful summer's day, and we watched them rounding Pinchgut. I asked Peter if he knew that tiny island's history, and he replied that he did. Peter seemed to know more about his adopted country than most Australians I came in contact with.

I tried to pick out an electric sign that used to fascinate me at night. It showed a tilted bottle of wine, from which wine poured realistically into a glass beneath it.

Watching the sparkling blue water, all the life and movement of the harbour, I thought if I only had the children with me, I'd want nothing else in the world. Then a cold shiver went through me. I thought: 'If John knew!' I remembered his mother's threats. And that memory suddenly made me doubt Peter. I'd always heard it said that men didn't respect the women they lived with. I lit a cigarette and blew out the smoke slowly and tried to sound 'hard-boiled'.

'Well, Valentino, where do we go from here?'

'What do you mean?'

'Men don't usually marry the women they sleep with, do they?'

I had never seen Peter look stern before and my heart soared as he said: 'Caddie! I don't like to hear you say that. I love you – more than ever now. I've already written asking my wife to divorce me.'

I dropped my cynical tone. 'Why, Peter, it might take years,' I said forlornly. 'After all, divorce isn't easy even supposing both parties are co-operative.'

He smiled gently and took both my hands in his.

'You're too pessimistic this morning, darling.'

'No, just facing up to facts.'

Then he brightened and changed the subject. He asked me if I would care to read the morning papers while he went to arrange with the landlady to have our dinner sent up. He explained that he always got his own breakfast, and arranged to have his other meals brought to the flat when required.

After luncheon, Peter went downstairs and got the car out while I put the finishing touches to my make-up. Then we went to see the children. When I saw the three of them talking together absorbedly, I really believe I had never known such deep and satisfying happiness in my life.

32

Christmas came and I was told that I could take Terry and Ann home for the holidays.

Peter rented a nice flat for us overlooking the harbour.

I gave up my job so I could spend as much time with them as possible; those were the happiest weeks I had spent for a long time, a holiday for me as well as the children. Trips to the Zoo, long drives in the car with Peter, visits to the Gardens and every place I could think of that would interest Terry and Ann.

Peter spent the evenings with us. He would arrive laden with fruit and sweets for the children and sometimes he would bring a book for me, and always flowers.

He was very fond of children, and once told me it had been a great disappointment to him when he learnt that his wife could not have children. It was fun to watch him tucking the table napkin under Ann's chin, showing her how to use her spoon correctly, or fixing Terry's shoelaces – little things perhaps, but things that John would never have thought of doing. It was fun to watch him romping with Terry and playing the role of father generally to my fatherless youngsters.

Ann, who was very fond of him, got to calling him Daddy, which, of course, pleased him immensely. Terry called him Peter.

I used to think sometimes, as I watched them, how much more like a real marriage my relationship with Peter was than my legal marriage to John had been.

But it came to an end only too soon.

After several months of anxious waiting Peter received a letter from his wife. She would not divorce him. Her church, the disgrace to her family, made it impossible. But he was hopeful that she would change her mind, and wrote to her again and again pointing out the futility of their marriage. Then her letters ceased. Although she had money of her own, Peter continued to send her an allowance each month, which she didn't even trouble to acknowledge.

At last the day came for me to part with the children again. Terry was quiet and seemed a little sad, and kept close to me while I packed and prepared for the trip to the Homes.

Peter waited in the car with Ann while I took Terry in to Miss Monty. There was a distressing scene as I handed him over to her. He cried and clung to my dress begging me piteously not to leave him. Miss Monty signed for me to leave. As I fled down the drive towards the waiting car I could hear his screams through the open french windows, and Miss Monty's booming voice commanding him to be quiet.

Ann showed no outward signs of emotion as I handed her

over to her matron, but she said goodbye in a tiny, tremulous voice, and waved a hand slowly and uncertainly to us as we drove away.

Peter was most sympathetic and offered to help me in a practical way. He asked me to let him make a permanent home for us; for me to live with him so that I could have the children with me always. Here was a chance for me to have a settled comfortable life, but I dared not accept, for I knew that if John got to know that I was living with Peter, or that he was keeping us, he and his mother would fight to get the children. It was too big a risk to take.

It was in the following winter that Peter received a cable-gram from his father. He was ill, tired out. Would Peter return to Athens and take over the responsibility of his business.

'It might be just a trick to get you back.'

He shook his head; his father would not do such a thing.

I had a sudden horrible suspicion and blurted out: 'Have you made it up with her?'

'Caddie, I'm surprised that you say that,' he said, and he looked so upset that, near to tears, I kissed him and asked to be forgiven.

'Must you go?' I asked.

'Yes,' he said slowly, 'I must go, for after all, I do owe my father something. Besides, it will give me an opportunity to talk things over with my wife. You know people of my country are slow to think of divorce, but I feel certain that she'll eventually see my point of view.'

'I have my doubts about that,' I said pessimistically, think-ing of the lonely time ahead. 'When do you intend going?'

He took my hands and, drawing me down beside him, began to tell me his plan.

'As soon as I can wind up my business here. The sooner I go, the sooner I get back to you.'

He talked on and on, telling me of his undying love for me, that he loved Terry and Ann as if they were his own, and assuring me that he would be back in a year, perhaps sooner. We talked well into the night.

All his endearing words failed to comfort me. I was miser-able, unhappy. He was leaving me and might never come back.

I thought of John when he told me he didn't want me any more. I'd been grief-stricken, and wondered how I was going to live without him. Now with my love of my children first in my mind, greater even than my love for Peter, I wondered how I was going to manage without him. I was to miss his love and his strength. But I was to miss, also, his help.

Within a few weeks he sailed for Athens, and I went back to a kennel at the Cross. But I couldn't bear being entirely alone and decided to take a plunge.

Peter had given me fifty pounds the day before he sailed, so I decided to go into business. Fifty pounds was little enough to start a business with even in those days; but I had often heard of people who had started with nothing and had ended up in a big way. Anyway, I argued with myself, it would be bad luck if I couldn't make as much as, or even more than, I could possibly earn by working for a boss.

I found a small shop and dwelling crammed in between a sausage factory and a second-hand shop, and which was situated in one of the poorest parts of the eastern suburbs; hemmed in by a network of narrow streets and laneways, where little children played unbiased with their coloured playmates. Here I had hoped to make some sort of a home for myself and the children, where we might live a happy, normal life together, something I yearned for more than anything in the world.

As I cleaned and painted the shop I made my plans. I would keep it a secret from Terry and Ann until I could get the business into top gear, then I'd tell them. I smiled as I thought of the pleasure I'd get out of watching their little faces light up when I told them the good news.

By the end of the first week I had the shop stocked with sweets, cool drinks and fruit and vegetables. Then I opened the doors to business.

From the word go it was an uphill battle. I was to encounter fierce competition from the big shop on the corner of the street. It was owned by an Italian who had several shops in and around the city. He bought everything in bulk, and was able to slash his prices, something I couldn't afford to do.

In order to keep what customers I had I pandered to them to some extent, and gave them credit whenever they asked for it. This was sheer folly and proved my undoing. Some of them were honest and paid me every penny they owed, while others ran up bills and refused to pay me anything and eventually took their custom elsewhere.

In an effort to recoup my losses I worked harder than ever. My day began at 6 a.m. and ended at midnight. Two mornings a week I rose at 4 a.m. and went to the markets to buy fruit and vegetables, which I paid a carrier to deliver to the shop. Despite all this, at the end of five months I was broke.

I was just about to close the doors, when a man walked in. He was a stranger to me. Thinking he wanted to buy something I went behind the counter. He was stockily built, bronzed and sunburnt. He told me he was from the country and was looking for an empty shop which he understood was to be let somewhere in that street. Did I know where it could be? I told him I knew of no empty shop anywhere about there, and, on the spur of the moment, added: 'I'll sell you this business if you like.'

He said something about having his mind set on an empty shop.

'Well,' I replied, looking around at the empty lollie jars, and a few bottles of soft drinks, 'this is almost empty.'

'How much are you asking for it?' he asked cautiously.

'What do you say to twenty-five?' I replied, explaining it would be on a walk-in, walk-out basis.

He looked down at the floor, squeezing his bottom lip with a finger and thumb. His eyes wandered around the shop, then back to me. He said: 'Wot about making it twenty quid?'

I thought for a moment, then said, 'Very well, I'll take twenty.'

He told me he'd just come from Booligal, and asked me if I knew where it was. I shook my head. He laughed. 'Surely you've heard of Hay, hell and Booligal?'

I remembered then. It was a place of heat, dust and flies. 'Yes,' I said, smiling. 'I've heard of it.'

'Yairs,' he drawled, 'so's most everybody.'

He told me he had been several years erecting rabbit-proof fences* around sheep stations; that his wife was sick, and that the bush doctor was puzzled about her case and had advised him to bring her to Sydney to consult a Macquarie Street specialist. It was his idea to look around for a shop in which to start a business instead of taking his wife back to Booligal. 'So I thought I'd kill two birds with the one stone, so to speak, and while she's visiting the quack I came along here to find this empty shop.'

I was hoping he'd hand over the money and settle the deal,

* In Australia, rabbits, introduced from England, spread so quickly that today they are present by the scores of millions. They are at once a pest and a valuable export.

but he said, 'Of course I'll have to talk it over with me wife first, you understand. She doesn't like the city, so I'll have to break it gently to her.'

With which remark he rose, saying he'd better be off, that he wouldn't be long, and hurried out of the shop.

I began straightening things up, thinking how lucky I would be if I got twenty pounds. At least I'd get some of my money back. Better than walking out broke.

I pulled the few remaining bottles of drinks forward on the shelves to make a better show and I removed some withered vegetables from off a rack near the door.

The time passed well into the afternoon, and I was about to give up hope of seeing him again when in he walked, his wife trailing behind him. She was little and scrawny, with a wizened face reflecting something of the hard life she had endured out West. There was the glint of battle in her dark eyes as her husband introduced us. She gave a quick nod, then glanced suspiciously around the shop, obviously not impressed by what she saw. Then she began to protest. She didn't want a shop. Whatever put that silly idea into his head, anyway?

She sat down, panting a little. 'How do you think I'm going to do in a shop. Me sick and all?'

'But it'll be me that'll be doing it all, not you,' he assured her.

Putting his thumbs in the armholes of his waistcoat he began painting a rosy picture to her of the possibilities of making a good business out of it; that he would stock everything from a needle to an anchor. It was obvious that he was keen on the idea, and as he talked of his plans one would have thought he was about to purchase Anthony Horderns* instead of this mean little shop which was doomed to failure whoever owned it. If I'd been honest I would have told them both to go back to where they came from and forget it, but I couldn't afford to be honest, and I wanted badly to get that twenty pounds.

He assured her she'd have everything she could wish for, see as many doctors as she liked, and go to the pictures as often as she wanted to. At this stage, I tactfully withdrew leaving them to talk it over. When I returned a few minutes later it was all settled. She had grudgingly consented.

He fumbled in his pockets and drew out two ten-pound notes which he placed on the counter while I proceeded to write out the receipt.

* One of Australia's oldest and biggest department stores.

Next thing was to have the tenancy transferred to him. His wife suggested that she'd stay and mind the shop while we went to the agent to have the shop tenancy transferred. The agent was agreeable, needless to say, as he was glad to have the shop tenanted. But there was a little matter of two pounds transfer fees, he explained politely. I had no alternative but to pay it. Then I walked out of his office with £18 in my purse, a feeling of disgust at the mean trick I'd played on the bushman and the prospect of job-hunting ahead of me once more. I'd had a letter from Peter that morning in which he recalled our happy times together and I re-read it to keep up my courage.

33

The loss of the business threw me back into the state of depression I'd been in when Peter went away. I suffered much more keenly than I had over the break-up of my marriage with John. Indeed I had much more to regret personally, for with Peter I had known, for the first time, the joy of real companionship as well as of love that put me and the children first. To add to my misery, I found it wasn't easy to get a job.

Fortunately I hadn't taken the children from the Homes. Things were getting tough – not only for little businesses like mine. It was just about then that people began to talk about the depression but I didn't realize what it really meant till I found how hard jobs were to get. Wages were being cut and tips dwindled.

I found I couldn't pay room-rent, keep myself and the children on my wages, and decided to get a job where I could live on the premises. By living in I would save on rent, fares and food, for which about fourteen shillings per week was deducted from my pay.

I eventually landed a job in a suburban hotel. When I arrived a barman directed me upstairs, and told me the Missus was expecting me.

The stairs were covered with a thick axminster carpet, and the banisters were of some rich polished wood. Reaching the landing I noticed that the rest of the house seemed in keeping with the stairs. Beautiful carpets ran the length of a wide hall, and oriental tapestries adorned smooth white walls. Several bedrooms flaunted their expensive furnishings through open doorways as I walked slowly along, not sure where I was intended to go. They were supposedly for guests but were never tenanted.*

A woman came from a room at the end of the hall. She was small and neat, and spoke in a soft, cultured voice as she ushered me into the presence of the Missus.

We entered a bedroom fit for a queen. . . . The ceiling was painted blue, and was sprinkled with silver stars to represent the sky on a starry night. I thought of the pictures I'd seen of film stars' bedrooms, but the face peering over a mauve satin quilt was anything but that of a film star. The face told me to take a seat. Then the pleasant-faced woman, whom I later learnt was Miss Coty, left, closing the door gently behind her.

I sat on the edge of a chair, and had a close-up of my prospective boss. Her eyes were the colour of sultanas, but perfectly round, and were held apart by a hooked nose. I could see she was middle-aged. Her voice was brittle and cracked occasionally as she questioned me closely on my previous job and why I'd left it. Then she proceeded to acquaint me with the rules of her hotel. She told me that employees were strictly forbidden to visit each other in their rooms, and that we were not to get into conversation with each other. How we were to work together without speaking was a point that bothered me, but I thought it wiser not to start asking questions.

A few more questions and I found myself engaged to start next morning. She closed the interview with the remark that if one wanted to keep one's job with her one would do well to bear her advice in mind. I left in as humble a manner as possible, telling myself as I went down the stairs that this job would be a bit of a problem. Events proved me right.

The Missus rose from what I later learnt was her periodic indisposition and came downstairs to make our lives a misery. Mean and petty, she seemed to delight in making trouble by interfering in the most stupid way. She would change our roster of working hours repeatedly, for no other reason than to cause us inconvenience, and would switch our afternoons off until it was impossible to make any but last minute arrange-

* Australian city hotels are, in the main, substantial structures of several floors. But the rooms are rarely occupied even in a period of severe housing shortage.

ments to go anywhere, or do anything. It was just that she liked to throw her weight about.

She literally loved money; on the occasions when she would come down to the bar she would sit at the till for hours with handfuls of coins, picking them up like a hen pecking wheat and letting them slip through her fingers lovingly. The customers used to watch her, and the things they said about her were libellous. But, of course, she never heard them.

There were two barmaids, one in the saloon bar and one in the public bar, one casual who worked on Fridays and Saturdays, and a barman-cellarman who completed the outfit. In the house there was a housemaid and a cook-laundress. The latter checked out the day I started.

I got used to seeing a new face in the kitchen every few weeks. Sometimes two or three cooks would come and go in that period. This was due to the Missus's meanness and her little habit of locking the refrigerator so that the cook was compelled continually to go to her to have it opened. A special lock had been fitted for this purpose.

Miss Coty was a sort of companion-secretary and boot-licker to the Missus, but a decent enough sort in her own way. She seemed loyal to the Missus and would smile indulgently whenever anyone remarked on her shortcomings in front of her. Often during the few minutes off I would spend in my room, the Missus would send Miss Coty up to tell me I was needed in the bar, as it had become busy. I had no alternative but to go, for I didn't want to lose my job, as living-in was so important to me.

Ivy, the housemaid, was a big girl in her late teens. She made no secret of the fact that she despised the Missus. She told me what to expect when I first started. She informed me of the real reason why the Missus didn't approve of the staff talking to one another. It was because she was paying less than award rates to some of the staff, a fact which would come to light if her employees compared notes. It said little for her intelligence that she imagined we would never talk together.

Although money was deducted from our wages for bed and board we were literally starved, and Ivy had organized the staff to throw in a few shillings each week to buy extra food outside.

'Lousy bastards!' Ivy snorted when she first told me about the arrangement. 'This pub's a goldmine and they own three others in the country as well.'

I was surprised to hear that as I knew it wasn't allowed.*
'Allowed!' Ivy laughed. 'Listen, sister, anything's allowed in this game, so my Dad reckons.'

I said I knew that was true so far as running a hotel was concerned, but after all the Law said –

Ivy laughed again. 'You're a real innocent. Pub-keepers make their own laws and even if the police wanted to do anything about it the politicians'd stop 'em.'

'But how do they get round the licences?'

'Aw, they get over that hurdle by putting in a dummy. When the boss put the hard word on me I said I'd come across if he'd put my name over the door of one of his hotels. But he was too fly for that.'

The boss turned up unexpectedly one day. We only saw him occasionally, thank heaven. The bond between him and his wife seemed to be entirely one of finance. They both were money-hungry. He was always trying to flirt with whichever female of the staff he could corner, though he was small and fat, and old enough to know better. Ivy gave me the oil about him.

'Better look out for the old ram, he walks in his sleep,' she remarked.

'Oh, well, that won't worry me; I'll lock my door.'

She chuckled: 'Oh yeah! He's got a master key, and he'll blow in on you as though he had a perfect right!'

'Oh,' I said, thoughtfully.

One Saturday night the Missus and the staff had gone out. I was alone in the house, or at least I thought I was. It was unpleasantly warm, and I'd had a cold shower and was lying on my bed, nude except for a sheet which I'd drawn up around my shoulders. I was reading Peter's latest letter and shedding a few tears over it when my bedroom door opened slowly, and the ram came in. I hadn't heard the key in the lock, for just then a train had roared past, deadening the sound.

'What do *you* want?' I demanded.

He moved to the end of the iron bed and leant casually against the brasswork top. 'I found no one about, then I saw your light, so I thought I'd come in for a while,' he said calmly, a lewd glint in his eyes.

* Despite the clause in the Act which specifically excludes multiple ownership, etc., it was disclosed at the Royal Commission that some hotel-keepers own as many as seven hotels.

'You've no right to come into my room like this; no right to come in here at all,' I protested.

He just stood there grinning and drew a pair of silk stockings out of the pocket of his dressing-gown. 'These are for you, provided you let me put them on you.'

He walked around the bed and stood in front of me holding the stockings aloft.

I was scared now, and instinctively drew the sheet more firmly about me.

'Get out of here!' I shouted.

He only laughed. 'You women, you make too much fuss about these things. What's it for, anyway?' He came closer. 'Come on, move over,' he said, coaxingly.

I sprang out of bed holding the sheet against my breasts with one hand, while with the other I began to push him towards the door, and threatened to tell his wife.

He merely shrugged his shoulders. 'Don't worry about her, she doesn't mind.'

He went to catch hold of me, and I tried to pull my knee up, but my feet got angled up in the sheet. He looked past me and grinned, for he could see the reflection of my naked back in the wardrobe mirror. I gave him one more vicious push towards the door.

He went quietly, taking the stockings with him. I slammed the door and put the dressing-table hard up against it.

One Sunday the Missus was giving a party, and asked me if I would help Ivy wait at table. I decided to forego my visit to the children, thinking that the extra money would be a godsend. We were also looking forward to a good feed as we heard the Missus tell the cook: 'Order what you like. We must have the best, even the best is not good enough for us. If you need fifty dozen eggs then order them – the sky is the limit.'

There were to be fifty guests, and I agreed to start at eight o'clock in the morning. Going down to the kitchen I found Ivy and the cook preparing food, while Miss Coty was in the dining-room arranging flowers on the tables, which were already set. I had never seen so much table ware before. Everything was of the best, from silver fish works to silver-gilt fruit knives. The tablecloths were of lace.

Ivy called me back to the kitchen and I began helping her. The kitchen was crammed with food. There were loads of chickens, savouries, oysters, and two large cans of ice-cream, also fruit salad, besides a bucket of pure cream. I was amazed to think that anyone who could be so mean about food for us could put on a spread like this for guests. The cook was grumbling, as is the habit of cooks.

From then on we didn't stop; waiting at table, clearing dishes, washing up, serving afternoon teas and drinks for those who preferred them, and preparing tables for the evening meal. After supper, which was at ten o'clock, we finished cleaning up, groped our way wearily up the back stairs and went to bed exhausted.

Pay-day came. But there was no extra money in our pay envelopes. Ivy, the first to get hers nearly exploded. She dived inside to see the Missus and returned within a few minutes cursing loudly and fluently. Well, there was nothing we could do about it, except go to the Union. And that was out of the question. If it became known that we dared to go to the Union with a complaint we would, in all probability get the sack. Besides, our next employer would want to know where we'd worked before, and would ring the Missus for a reference. Our cake would be dough. Best way was to forget it.

That afternoon, Ivy came and told me she was leaving. 'Can't you hang on a little longer?' I asked.

'No, I've had enough of this place. If ever there was a bitch, it's that old cow. You wouldn't read about it, would you?'

Well, that was the Missus. She thought nothing of her staff, regarding them merely as instruments for making money; slaves to her comfort.

Dismissing the whole business from my mind I went downstairs to start work in the bar. I was happy enough there, provided the Missus didn't come in and upset things. The customers were a nice crowd and there was rarely any trouble. It was a nice middle-class suburb, only recently on the map. The bar was nicely laid out, its walls done with cream and green tiles and shiny fittings; but that didn't mean a thing when it was noted that the worst practices of less modern hotels were methodically carried out. Slop beer from the drip-trays was poured through a cloth into a bucket which had a tube attached carrying the beer to the cellar.* During this process tobacco and other waste would adhere to the cloth. Excessive

* Since 1939 the Law has demanded that a strong dye be placed on all drip-trays to discolour slop beer, and therefore stop this filthy practice. Recent disclosures show that some hotels have once more discarded the use of the dye.

collars on the beer, inferior spirits, and the usual skulduggeries were insisted on by the Missus.

There was a very posh lounge to attract the custom of women – flowers, soft lights, deep armchairs and higher prices. They had recently spent five thousand in carpets and the usual trimmings to make the lounge a luxury one to entice women to spend more time there.

The barmaid serving drinks in this luxury lounge repeatedly used dirty glasses – those that had been previously used by customers. She would pick them off the sink, and without even dipping them in the water, the froth still on them, she would serve to someone else. So much for the spreading of T.B. among other things.

Yet the Missus boasted of the way she ran this hotel! I used to wonder what Peter would think of it. He always said Australians had the most uncivilized drinking habits in the world.

Like every other pub, the place had its 'characters'. You soon get to know them when you've been around a bit. There's the fellow who wants to fight after three beers, usually taking off his coat and throwing it over the counter for safe keeping. He doesn't last long as a rule. There's the average chap who drinks his beer quietly, and as quietly leaves. Then the sport, who can give you the dinkum oil for Saturday. He's invariably broke.

In a class of his own is the hum. Some of these are casuals, temporarily out of cash, but with an unquenchable thirst. But it's the professional who merits recognition, for he has developed the technique of the bite until it is almost one of the arts. Entering a bar, he runs an experienced eye over the gathering, mentally noting the prospects. He has to decide which type of bite has the best chance with the prospect he selects. A few exchanges, and he either moves off, having pocketed a bob or, unabashed, makes tracks to the next prospect.

The speciality of the hum is the lone drunk. Most drunks love to talk, and the lone drunk is the worst of the lot. In all probability he will be talking to himself when the hum approaches. The hum stands alongside studiously ignoring the drunk, and calls for a beer. Unless he is right out of luck the drunk is bound to fasten eyes, badly out of focus, on him. 'Good day. Shay, don't I know you? Avva drink.'

'No, you have a drink with me,' says the hum, having no intention of paying if the victim accepts.

However, he takes little risk. The drunk is almost certain to say, 'No, you have it with me.' And so the hum is set for a steady spell of drinking.

I've seen few drunks who would not become offended if not allowed to shout the drinks and prepared to shout for the bar if it occurs to them. If their wives could only see them!

There seemed never to be any shortage of money in that bar, but little of it came the staff's way.

Growing tired of the bad conditions I decided to leave, and unfortunately mentioned my intention before some members of the staff. In due course it was carried back to the Missus who promptly sent Miss Coty to tell me that she wanted to see me.

I found her in bed, just like the first day I'd seen her. She raised herself on one elbow, and drawing the silken sheet up under her chin told me to take a seat.

She came straight to the point. 'I hear you intend leaving – is that true?'

'Yes,' I answered, feeling uneasy.

'You know you can't afford to pick and choose your jobs these days; you probably know that better than me,' she said meaningly.

'No, I suppose not.' I knew it to be the truth.

'What's wrong with keeping the job you have?" she asked, her eyes holding mine in a steady gaze.

Right then I wanted to ask her what's right with it? I wanted so much to tell her what I thought of her, her meanness, her nasty habits, and to ask her about all the overtime which was due to me. But I wasn't game, for jobs were scarce. I had to think of my children and I might need a reference from her for my next job. There was silence for a minute while I tried to make up my mind.

'Well, what do you say?'

I hesitated for a moment, then said: 'I'll stay.'

She reached out to get her glasses and newspaper off the table beside her bed saying, 'All right, you can go.'

I left her, and felt almost gay as I tripped downstairs. She had asked me to stay on. She knew I was worth something to her in the business. She hadn't promised me anything, but I thought surely now she'll do something about my overtime, give me a little extra pay, perhaps.

But conditions continued as bad as ever, and there was no extra money for me on pay-day. I grew more and more depressed. It looked as though I was never going to escape from this life which I suddenly began to loathe. There was nothing but talk of lost jobs in the bar. Everyone was on edge and tempers became short. The only comfort I had was my visits to the children and Peter's letters, which though as loving as ever were not very cheerful. From the way he avoided mentioning his divorce I knew his wife was being as difficult as ever.

At last I could stand the Missus no longer. Like Ivy and dozens of others I reached the limit of my endurance and walked out.

I tramped the streets from one hotel to another in search of a job, finally getting one in the city. The Missus here was not interfering or mean. She spent most of her time at beauty-parlours; and dieted to the extreme.

The building was very old, and besides accommodating the family and staff, afforded shelter to hundreds of rats. The rats rioted all over the place. Some of them played 'hide and seek' on the stairs or in hallways at night. They would pretend not to notice me as I made a run for my bedroom door. Once, while the cook and I were having tea at the kitchen table, two rats came out from a hole in the skirting-board and staged a fight under the table. We both left the kitchen in less time than it takes to wink. That night the cook packed and left.

I stood it for a year. Then the rats beat me and I left.

34

Had I known that the sequence of easy jobs had come to an end I probably would have stayed, rats or no rats. For by now the depression was really under way.

I soon owed rent, and arrears for the upkeep of the children were steadily mounting. The latter worried me more than anything else.

Limiting myself to one meal a day, I walked myself footsore looking for a job. Wherever one went, a snarl was all that could be expected of the boss. A written reference as well as a verbal one over the phone was insisted on by some of the bosses. They were certainly having their day! It was sheer waste of time going to the agencies now, as a black-market had sprung up, and only those in the know and who had the required fee were likely to land a job.

No longer able to afford the price of a paper, I walked into the city each morning and took my place in the queue of unemployed, eagerly waiting my turn to scan the situations vacant advertisements which from early times had been posted on the wall outside the *Herald* office.

At last I got a casual job in a city hotel and, with an occasional odd job, managed to exist. A year of this life, then I got a full-time job in a slum pub run by a young publican.

I hadn't heard from Peter for several months. I'd moved around so much his letters couldn't catch up with me. Finally, when they did catch up, there was quite a bundle of them.

It warmed my heart to read them and realize that he hadn't changed. Indeed he said that being away from me had made him love me more – if that was possible! I cried as he wrote about 'our' home and 'our' children. But important as all that was it didn't bring his return any closer. The depression had hit Greece too, and not only was his father ill, but the family business was in a bad way and needed all Peter's efforts to keep it going.

The only gleam of hope was that his wife seemed to have resigned herself to no longer living with him and he was hopeful of persuading her to free him altogether eventually. In the meantime he suggested that I should get a divorce as it might take a long time.

And a hell of a lot of money, I thought disconsolately, but by a stroke of luck I ran into Leslie a few days later and told her about it. She advised me to go to the Legal Aid Department which would help me out.

I was not quite as frightened of the Law as I had once been, so I plucked up courage and went along. If I had been paying a huge fee the clerk couldn't have been nicer or more helpful. And I found, for the first time, that even though I had technically 'deserted' John, the Law was on my side as he had given me grounds for doing so and had later been openly living with another woman. Where he was now I didn't know but I knew his mother's address would always find him for the service of papers.

Peter's reassurances and the advice of the clerk and the fact that my divorce was actually on its way must have gone to my head. Quite suddenly I was overwhelmed by the feeling that, without Peter, my life was so empty that I couldn't bear to be without the children, and I decided to get a cottage and make some sort of a home for them. Terry was now nine years old, and Ann two years younger. They were old enough for me to manage my work during the day while they were at school, and I felt that I could trust them to remain at home in the afternoons and early evenings until I could get home from work.

Such a decision at such a time really seems a bit insane when I look back on it. But at the time I was swept away by the need for love and companionship. When I told Leslie about my plan she shrugged her shoulders and said cynically: 'You're nuts. But I suppose it's better than taking to the bottle as other women do.'

Hearing of a small place to let not far from where I worked, I went along to see the agent. I was pleased to find that he was a regular customer at the pub, and was one of those who always liked me to serve him. This, I hoped, would be in my favour, for I had no reference or last week's rent receipt. I was right, for he let me the cottage, and didn't ask any difficult questions.

I went along and inspected the cottage which I found barely deserved the name. It had a thirty-foot frontage. It was weather-board and weather-beaten. The little wooden gate, hanging on one hinge, grated on the flagged path as I pushed it open. Taking the huge key the agent had given me, I inserted it in the front door lock. Neighbours from doorways and verandahs stared curiously at me as I opened the door and went in.

There was a short passage. In the first room, which was to be the bedroom, I noticed a gas-meter in one counter. It had been robbed of its contents, for the cash-box was lying on the floor, battered and empty. Either someone had broken in after the previous tenant had vacated the place, or the tenant had committed the theft. That sort of thing was quite common in those terrible days. Next room along the end of the passage was the living room, and the remaining one was the kitchen. The whole place reeked of dampness and mould. The floors were covered with newspapers, yellow with age, which had been used as a base for floor coverings.

The kitchen held an obsolete fuel stove with some of its parts missing, and a rickety shelf jammed in between the fireplace and the wall. A gas-ring with a length of rubber tubing stood on the side of the stove. There was no bathroom, just a laundry in the backyard with two tubs and a copper set in bricks. I decided we'd have to bathe in the copper. After all, one couldn't expect modern conveniences for fourteen shillings a week.

Working by candle-light for several nights I cleaned the place thoroughly. Then I went to a second-hand shop and bought a bed for seven and sixpence, also a mattress and one blanket. From the fruit shop across the way I bought several empty cases which I used for a table and chairs. The Missus where I worked gave me some old curtains which I dyed and pressed; by cutting away the rotted parts I managed to get enough sound pieces to cover my windows.

That was the first real home I provided for my children. Perhaps it was a mistake to take them away from where they were receiving such good care, but I had to learn from bitter experience.

When I went to fetch them, Ann was not anxious to leave and pleaded with me to allow her to have just one more play with her little mates on the lawn. But Terry was overjoyed when I told him I was taking him home with me that day. He clung to my hand, and stood silent while I talked to Miss Monty and the matron, who both wished us luck.

Coming home, I had a nasty jolt to see all the furniture from the house next door piled on the pavement. A woman was sitting on a pile of bedding nursing a baby, and the tears were running down her cheeks without her seeming to notice. There were two other children and a man with a long scar down one cheek. I noticed he had a Returned Soldier's Badge in the lapel of his shabby coat. There was such a look of hopelessness on his face that I hurried the children inside, not wishing to have to explain that the people had been evicted because they couldn't pay their rent. It was to become a common enough sight to them later!

Terry and Ann were both well-mannered and healthy, standing out from the neighbourhood children, who were ragged and dirty for the most part. They fell for a good deal of chaffing from their playmates, but they soon settled down.

I took them to the public school and had them enrolled. The headmaster seemed kind and showed great interest in the children, and in how I was placed when I told him their father did not provide for them.

A couple of days later four boys came from the school, carrying two venetian blinds and a table. They were from the headmaster. The table provided us with our main item of furniture.

I went to the school to inquire about the children's progress, and to thank the headmaster for his kindness. When I stood up to go he made a suggestion hardly in keeping with his important job. I gave him my reply in finest public bar style, and left. So it wasn't a kindly action after all!

Just as I was getting settled in my work and home the boss told me that he had sold out, and that the new licencee had arranged to bring his own staff, which meant that I would have to look for another job.

The useful, who had also been given the boot, told me the story of the young publican who was getting out into a swisher suburb.

He had been financed by his father and father-in-law on the understanding that he would pay them back when he got on his feet. He had managed the repayment more quickly than anyone anticipated.

Possessing an old car, he used to take customers and their children on short trips at week-ends. His customers thought him a wonderful chap and brought their friends to bend the elbow at his bar, and share the warmth of his hospitality.

That had been the picture for three years. Then came the day when he met his obligations – the first outward sign being a spanking new and expensive car at his door.

If any of the admiring customers flocking out to view this last word in cars ever expected to experience the luxury of its upholstery they were disappointed. A new name appeared on the door. Their young friend transferred himself to a brand new pub in a better-class suburb. The customers had served their purpose.

It's a pity customers can't hear some of the remarks passed about them over the pub-keeper's dinner-table. There'd be many a shock for those who think they are just it with the boss.

I once heard a publican's wife complaining about her husband taking scum to the races with him in the car. He replied that it was business.

That pub was in the slums, too, in a back street.

My next job was another casual, pay – thirty shillings a week.

Every week fourteen shillings for rent had to be paid in advance.

I applied to the Child Welfare Department for assistance for the children. The wheels of government departments move slowly, and I had to wait and hope. In the meantime it was a struggle for existence. Although customers seemed to consume just as much at the bar they seldom tipped now. Often there was nothing in the house for us to eat.

Then a letter came from the Department informing me that my case had been approved, and that a cheque would be forwarded in due course. Every morning I'd stand on the verandah watching for the postman, but he would look across at me and shake his head as he strode along.

The arrival of the cheque would be a godsend now, I thought, for I'd found myself with just enough to pay the rent that morning. The landlady was due to call, and I didn't dare spend the rent, for I knew she wouldn't hesitate to put us in the street.

The landlady always pulled up punctually at nine, driving her own car, and looking suspiciously over the cottage to see if we had been knocking it about. One good kick and it would have toppled over, anyway. As she wrote out a receipt she managed to swing her remarks over to politics. I gathered she didn't like the Labour Premier very much, but I offered no commiserations: I didn't own any property.

That night we ate our meal of stale bread and dripping, and weak tea without sugar or milk, then went to bed. It was bitterly cold and, as we hadn't any fuel, bed was the best place. But sleep was out of the question. Ann began to whimper, saying she was hungry. Terry said: 'You mustn't say that Ann, you know Mummy hasn't any money.'

That decided me.

I'd hoped we could get through the night, feeling sure the cheque would arrive next morning, but I couldn't bear to hear my child crying of hunger.

I got out of bed and dressed quickly not knowing exactly what I intended doing. I went across the road to the little corner shop, walked in as though I owned it, and asked the woman behind the counter for a loaf of bread, some porridge meal, sugar, and a jar of honey, then, remembering that I would need milk and had forgotten to bring the can, I asked the woman if she would lend me something in which to carry the milk home.

'Certainly. How much?' she asked.

'Make it two pints, please.'

As she whisked the goods on to the counter, I kept up a barrage of gossip in an endeavour to keep up my courage, and did not overlook the psychological value of saying what a nice little chap her little boy was, and how intelligent. I'd often seen him playing in front of the shop and thought him anything but intelligent.

When she had my order ready I casually bundled it under my arm, and the milk in my other hand, as she drew in her breath and reached for a pencil. 'Now, let me see. That will be . . . er,' and she started to tot a few figures on a scrap of paper. It was my turn to take a deep breath, and as I did so a small sign behind her caught my eye. It read, 'Please do not ask for credit as refusal often offends.'

'Er . . . oh, yes. I'll pay you in the morning for these. I get paid tomorrow, you know.' With that I walked calmly out of the shop, not daring to look back. She didn't call after me, so either she didn't mind, or was speechless at my hide!

As I walked home, I thought it was just as well that the woman had not tried to prevent me from taking the parcel of food, for I felt so desperate I'd have taken it anyway, even if the whole police force had been after me.

Terry and Ann were sitting up in bed when I entered, and their eyes popped when they saw the food. They tumbled out of bed and we hurried to the kitchen. I lit the gas-jet and put some porridge on to cook.

'While that's cooking I'll cut you both a nice piece of bread and honey,' I told them.

As they sat eating, I noticed the gas beginning to weaken. I looked around for the penny I knew wasn't there.

Terry called out, 'I know where there's a lemonade bottle, Mummy.' They scampered out into the yard, to return carrying a bottle.

'You take it over to the corner shop, Terry. Hurry, darling.'

Terry was back in a few minutes with the precious penny, and our meal was saved.

Next morning the cheque arrived. As the postman handed me the letter my first thought was to pay the woman in the corner shop, but on second thoughts I decided to cash it at the top shop, as I didn't want her to see that it was a Government cheque for the maintenance of my children. I wanted to keep my prestige with her as I didn't know when I might have to repeat last night's performance.

When I cashed the cheque I looked at the four pounds and

some shillings, and thought, 'This is wonderful. Gee, the Government's good. Four pounds for nothing,' thinking of how I'd have to work to get four pounds.

I found plenty to do with it. First of all I paid the woman at the corner shop for the groceries. She smilingly thanked me, and wanted to know if there was anything I wanted at the moment. From then on my name was good with her, and I was able to get tick whenever I asked for it. Terry needed a new pair of shoes, and Ann needed bloomers and some socks. I needed – well, there was so much I needed I decided to forget it.

There were many more of those hungry nights. I lost weight, and so did the children. That was the price we paid to be together, but it was worth it.

35

One morning while I was sweeping the front steps I looked up to see a policeman coming in the front gate. He asked me if I was Mrs Marsh. I said I was, and asked him to come in. The neighbours were inclined to sticky-beak and I didn't want them to know my business. I invited the policeman to take a seat. It was only a fruit case, and I watched anxiously as he sat down. He was a very big policeman.

Not noticing my concern for the case he drew out a bundle of papers from his tunic pocket, cleared his throat, and proceeded, 'I have some documents from the Child Welfare Department. I've been sent to find out the particulars of your income, if any.'

'Oh, yes,' I answered, wondering if this meant trouble.

He asked me a few questions, reading from a form he held in his hand. They were straightforward enough, and he elaborated on points here and there. He was very tactful and kind, and I answered his questions easily. But at the same time I was cautious, for I didn't want to incriminate myself.

'Now, Mrs Marsh,' he said, 'the Department is not satisfied that you've stated your income correctly. As you're in receipt of ten shillings per week for each of your two children, and you have stated to the Department that your rent is fourteen shillings per week, that leaves you only six shillings for food and clothing. The Department is concerned in the welfare of your children – that's what they're for – and they know you couldn't possibly support them on six shillings a week.'

I flushed guiltily, feeling sure he couldn't fail to notice. Had they found out that I was earning a few extra shillings? That would mean the end of the cheques, I thought despairingly. I didn't mean to put it over the Government, but wasn't sure how much I would be permitted to earn, and still be entitled to Government aid. The appalling Permissible Income Regulations* worried me greatly, as they did everybody else.

The policeman was speaking. 'The position is this; the Department want you to register for the dole.'

'The dole!' I exclaimed, and began to cry a little. The dole! What a blow to one's pride. During the good years people on the dole were looked upon as outcasts, little better than the dogs on the streets.

'Me get the dole? Never.' I sobbed, shocked at the idea. 'Why should they worry about me? I'm the children's mother. Do you think I'd let them starve?'

'It isn't a question of what I think; it's the law,' he answered, not unkindly.

Then he reasoned with me, saying it was no disgrace to accept the dole; that scores of thousands were getting it, anyway.

'I couldn't bear to walk into a dole office,' I protested. 'I wouldn't have the nerve.'

'Well,' he said, 'if you don't get the dole I am afraid the Welfare Department will stop payments to you.'

With that I sobbed aloud knowing that whatever happened I couldn't afford to lose those cheques, as I'd got to rely on them so much. I gazed despondently at him.

'I'll tell you what!' he said. 'I'll go to the dole office now and fix it up for you, and bring you your first issue. All you will have to do is sign the papers, then, when the next issuing day comes around, you just walk right into the dole office and let them stamp your card.'

I thanked him, wondering why he should take all this trouble for me.

Two hours later he returned with the papers which I signed, and handed me my dole card, assuring me that everything would be all right. I thanked him again, and he left.

A fortnight passed and I found my way to the dole office,

* i.e. Means Test.

self-consciously hurrying into the building for fear of someone I knew seeing me. I felt ashamed to think I'd come down
to this. Signs directed me into an office with a low counter running the length of the room. Behind the counter were several
clerks. I'd made a point of being early, but a queue of men and
women had already began to pile up. However, after waiting
about an hour my turn came.

I stepped to the counter as the senior clerk came towards
me. From a book of tickets he began writing and asking me
my name and full particulars, also the name of the trades-
people to whom I intended to give my dole tickets. I named
a butcher on Main Street, and a grocer and baker, for which
the clerk gave me three tickets which were joined by per-
forated edges.

Next day I went to do some washing for Mrs Burnley, a
woman living in the upper end of the district. She was a lucky
woman, for her husband was a well-paid government em-
ployee, having a steady job in some department or other.
Although she was a big, strong woman, she liked to have her
washing done for her. I was to be paid three shillings for a
half-day's work. After greeting me, she told me that I would
find everything in the basket. I certainly did – even to junior's
nappies and three heavy blankets. I knew that I was being
exploited but that three shillings was vital to my budget.

I lit the copper and began washing. Before I'd got properly
started I felt tired and little beads of perspiration stood out
around my mouth, but I had to keep going. About half-past
ten Mrs Burnley came out in her dressing-gown, a cigarette
drooping from her mouth, her hair untidy. Throwing a bundle of soiled linen at my feet she said languidly: 'Here's
another lot I missed. I just put the kettle on; I suppose you
could do with a cup of tea?'

'Too right! I'll be in as soon as I finish this tub.'

I sat down at the table as Mrs Burnley cleared the dirty
dishes off the table into the sink. Burnley junior crawled about
the floor, painting it with his wet nappie. He started to squall.
His mother banged the teapot on the table, reached for a
brown paper bag from the mantlepiece and withdrew a couple
of chocolates.

'Anything for a quiet life,' she sighed, smiling at me as she
pushed a chocolate into each of his hands.

The wailing ceased immediately and she sat down and began
to pour the tea. We watched junior cram one chocolate into

his mouth, and then try to force the other in. His face was soon a sticky mess.

After drinking my tea I returned to the laundry. Mrs Burnley followed on to the verandah, junior with her. As I washed I could see her lying on a sofa, a novel claiming her rapt attention. As she read, a leisurely hand wandered from time to time to the bag of chocolates beside her, sometimes pausing in mid-air as a particularly enthralling passage took precedence over her palate.

At last I finished the washing, and thankfully changed into my street frock and shoes. Walking out on to the verandah I told her I had finished and was going.

She dragged her eyes away from her novel: 'Finished already? Gee, it didn't take you long. Er . . . I wonder if you would do the washing up for me?'

When she saw my reluctance she went on, 'I'll pay you an extra shilling, if you will.'

I said I would do it and went to the sink. Every shilling counted.

Coming from Mrs Burnley's I turned the corner of my street to see the rabbit-o's* horse and cart standing outside my gate. I bought a rabbit, handing him a shilling from the money I'd just earned from Mrs Burnley. I went inside to get a plate. When I came out again he was standing on my verandah with a rabbit in his hand.

Handing me the rabbit, he counted six pennies out to me with a blood-stained hand. He was a little man, talkative, and full of brisk business. He was the true dealer type.

'Ya must be noo ter this place, lady?'

'Yes, we haven't been here very long.'

'Well, I come around 'ere every week. On a Toosday.'

'Goodo, I'll get another from you next week.'

But the next week I was broke. I went to the door on hearing his call, 'Wile rabbee, wile rabbee', ready to tell him that I wouldn't be wanting any from him that day.

'Gorn, take it, missus,' he said, pushing the rabbit into my hands.

I protested, but he cut me short with, 'You can pay me next time.'

Looking at the uncertain expression on my face he broke into a laugh. 'Why, y'ain't goin' ter do a moonlight flit, are yer?'

* An itinerant street seller of rabbits.

146

'No, it's not that. It's just that I mightn't have the money to pay you next time, either,' I told him.

He became serious. 'Is it as bad as all that?'

I nodded.

'No ol' man?' he asked sympathetically.

'No,' I said shortly, pushing my resentment at his question aside, realizing that he wasn't merely inquisitive.

'I lost him,' I said in a flat voice.

'Dead?' he asked.

I did not answer, letting him get the impression that he was right.

'Sorry,' he said.

I let people think I was a widow. It was the easiest way out of it.

36

Dole day dawned again. I gave the children their breakfast and packed them off to school. With nothing to give them for their lunches, I told them to come home for their lunch, hoping to get away from the dole office before that time. Terry was willing to come home, but Ann was worried: she was thinking of the extra wear and tear on her shoes which were nearly worn out.

'Besides, Mummy, I'll be late for school. It's too far to come home,' she complained.

Terry reasoned with her, and finally she agreed that she could make it.

I approached the dole office as nervously as on my first visit. Long before I had reached there I could see the crowd of people clustered on the footpaths outside. When I drew closer I was surprised to see some of my neighbours, and several faces from the bar where I worked. A Mrs Yardley, who lived next door to me, smiled and nodded, and came over for a chat. She put me wise to a few things around the office, and I was particularly interested when she told me there was a committee there which issued free fruit and vegetables every Friday.

'An' listen. If ya want anything from the Gove'ment, go an' see our local Member. But take a tip from me an' don' tell 'im too much. If yer 'appen ter be earnin' a few shillin's on the side whatever yer do keep it under yer hat.' She winked shrewdly as she moved away to take her place in the queue.

I noticed the rabbit-o earnestly in conversation with another man. He saw me and nodded as he resumed his conversation. So, I thought, even the rabbit-o was on the dole.

I looked at the line-up: women with pinched anxious faces, patched clothes; men with that lost sort of look the unemployed get. Their shirts threadbare but clean, all with their heels well down and some with their soles almost hanging off their feet. All – men and women – with that unhealthy pasty colour and bad teeth they couldn't afford to get attended to.

I felt more sorry for the men, somehow. I found that men on the whole felt worse about things than women. For a man there was always the feeling of personal failure in losing his job even though it wasn't his fault. And all most of them wanted was a job and a chance to earn a living – not this humiliating charity.

With seventeen and sixpence dole ration for the three of us, one pound from the Welfare Department, and fifteen shillings which I earned as casual barmaid, I still found it difficult to manage.

Next afternoon a knock summoned me to my front door. I opened it to find the rabbit-o standing there, a chaff bag slung over his shoulder. 'Good day, missus. I brought yer some fruit and veges they wus givin' away up at the 'all, an' knowin' yer didn't 'ave no ol' man ter git yours for ya I thought as 'ow I'd git 'em 'an bring 'em down for yer.'

I didn't know what to say. I couldn't be sure of his motives. Unselfish people came rarely in this world.

He must have read my thoughts, for he said: 'I'm fair dinkum all right.'

I thanked him, hesitatingly, and asked him to bring them inside. I felt ashamed to invite anyone into the home. Its bare, uncovered floors, and few miserable sticks of furniture were something to hide.

He carried the bag through to the kitchen and tipped the contents on to the floor. 'There's not much there but it's sumthin'.'

A few potatoes, a tiny cabbage, a couple of shrivelled carrots, and a dozen or so mandarins not much bigger than marbles fell to the floor.

I asked him if he would care for a cup of tea. He accepted saying he'd never been known to knock back a cup of tea in his life.

He sat down on one of our 'chairs' – the one that had successfully withstood the weight of the policeman – while I put the saucepan I used for a kettle on the gas-ring.

I still felt I couldn't be too sure of him when, reading my thoughts, he said, 'Yer know, yer got nuthin' ter be afraid of – wimmen don' interest me any more.'

'Don't mean to tell me you're a woman-hater?' I said laughingly.

'No, it ain't that . . . I got a mother an' two sisters. But I lorst me wife over five years ago, an' no one 'as taken 'er place, an' no one ever will. She died 'avin' our first.'

I told him of Terry and Ann.

He began to drink his tea. 'Ya know missus, yer lucky havin' two kids. I've got nothin'.' The tears rolled down his weather-beaten face, and he brushed them away unashamed. 'If on'y the nipper 'ad lived, then I'd 'ave 'ad sumthin' of 'ers and mine ter battle for.'

At that moment Ann came bursting in from school. I could see she was excited. As she came over and kissed me I said, 'Ann, this is Mr Sutton. He has been very kind to us, he brought us these nice vegetables and fruit.'

Mr Sutton had restored his face to normal, and smiled and nodded as Ann said politely, 'How do you do, Mr Sutton?'

'My! Wot a nice youngster. Real good-lookin' too.'

I smiled, and told Ann to wash her hands and I'd give her a piece of bread.

'May I have butter and syrup, please, Mummy?'

'No, dear, we can't afford both.'

Mr Sutton chuckled, saying, 'Gorn! Give it to 'er, bless 'er little 'eart.'

He lifted himself off the fruit case: 'S'pose I'd better be orf now; gotta see a man about a dog.'

'Thanks again for bringing the vegetables and fruit, Mr Sutton,' I said.

'Aw, don't mention it. The pleasure's all mine. Hoo-roo!' He made his way through the hall to the front door.

37

A couple of weeks off work nursing Terry and Ann, who picked up a bad form of flu that was going round, threw all my budget out. For the first time I couldn't pay my rent and when, in fear and trembling, I told the landlady I was astonished to hear her say: 'The Government will give you monetary assistance, so go along to the office in Macquarie Street. The entrance is next to the Mint. Give them my name and address and I'll support whatever you say.' She went out to the car, calling over her shoulder: 'The more you say you owe, the better.'

Well, I started off to Macquarie Street, and a long walk it was. I only had threepence in the world, so I walked from Paddington, keeping the money to pay my tram fare home. When I got there a queue, much like the dole queue, had formed, which meant a long wait. I waited for several hours before my turn came.

A young man wearing an alpaca coat with the elbows out, and with ink-stained fingers, began asking me questions: my father's name, mother's maiden name, who was my grannie, and a lot of stuff that sounded irrelevant to me. He asked me how much rent I owed, like the others (who had already put me wise) I made out I owed much more than I did.

A woman near nudged me and whispered in my ear as the man bent down to get a form from under the counter. She said, 'Tell 'im yer owe twenty quid.' So I did.

There was another woman sitting on a form near the counter; she was feeding a child at her breast. I had thought that judging by the size of the child, it should have been weaned long ago, but I heard its mother telling the woman next to her, that although he was nearly two she still kept him on the breast because it was one less mouth to feed. She looked as though she was suffering from malnutrition.

I left there somewhat contented, thinking to myself that now I would have 22/6 per month extra . . . what a blessing that would be. . . .

But I found out much later that it wasn't as good as it seemed, as the Government did not work things for us as easy as that.

When the second payment was due I waited in vain for the cheque, and when it did not come I went back to see why.

There was the same queue, looking more depressed than ever. It was the same man behind the counter in the same alpaca coat. I told him I received the first cheque, but the second one had not arrived. He asked me if I had re-applied. I told him no I hadn't. I did not think it necessary. I became a little heated, and asked him why he hadn't told me the first time I came. He got nasty and said something about him not being there to answer questions. He was there to ask them. The crowd milling around the counter were listening in to this, and a little fellow got a bit cocky and chipped the clerk, saying something about if it wasn't for the likes of us he wouldn't have a job. The clerk gave a smirk at this, which seemed to provoke the crowd, and one man threatened to pull him over the counter and job him. There was confusion for a while, then the clerk threatened to eject the lot of us. After that everyone cooled down, and business was resumed. I was asked the same questions all over again: my father's name, where he was born, my mother's name, and my grannie's, etc. After that turn-out I gave up applying for monetary assistance. There was a bit too much red tape in having to go through this rigmarole every month. I could make more doing a few extra jobs at the pub even if it meant long hours, and I wasn't treated like a beggar.

One Saturday afternoon I was busy washing glasses in the bar when in walked the senior clerk from the dole office. I looked around hurriedly to see if anyone else was going to serve him but I was the only one at that end of the bar. It was too late, anyway, for he called to me for a beer. He showed no signs of recognition as I placed the beer before him, and he drank it and walked out.

I had the breeze up properly. *Now* there would be a blue I thought despairingly. I was not supposed to be working, and feared the worst. The very least that could happen would be that I would lose the dole.

My thoughts were interrupted as a group of men came into the bar. One suddenly said, 'Well, strike me handsome! It's Caddie!'

I recognized him as Chilla, a customer of Mrs Smith.

'Where have you been keeping yourself all this time, Caddie?'

'Oh,' I laughed, 'just poking around.'

I was pleased to see them, and as we talked I forgot my worries. They were a fine crowd. He told me the news: that Mrs Smith had retired from business, that Ted the bookie was still betting around the pub, that he was married now and had a couple of kiddies.

'Yes. He married a sheila called Maudie.'

So, I thought, Maudie *did* get her man after all.

Bill, the rabbit-o, came in soon afterwards. He, too, seemed pleased to see me. He was carrying a wooden box containing a dressed chicken, a cauliflower, a tin of Nestlé's cream and a tin of peaches, and explained that he was going to raffle them in the bar. My friends bought several tickets, and Bill moved off around the bar calling out, not too loudly: ' 'Oo wants a ticket in the raffle? Come on, gents, be in it. Ya've got to speculate to accumalate.' He did a brisk business.

Right on six o'clock that night he placed all the butts from his book into his hat, shook them up energetically, then placed the hat before me on the counter.

'Come on, Missus, you draw the winner.'

I put my hand into the hat and drew out a little ball of paper, which I passed to Bill. He unscrewed it, looked, then called out: 'Number eighty-seven. 'Oo's got the lucky number? Number eighty-seven, gents.'

One of my friends from Mrs Smith looked at his ticket and grinned. 'Here it is, digger. Number eighty-seven.'

Bill took the proffered ticket, examined it carefully, then slid the box on to the counter. 'There she is. All fair an' above board.'

The winner looked at me and said, 'You'd better take it, Caddie.'

I said, 'Don't be silly, you take it home to your wife.'

'What wife?' he said dryly.

One of his cobbers said: 'He hasn't got himself a ball and chain yet, have you, Chilla?'

Chilla replied, 'No, I can't keep myself, let alone a wife,' and they all laughed.

Bill Sutton said, 'I'll carry it 'ome fer yer, Missus. They'll be too 'eavy for yer.'

The bar was stifling by the time the useful called beseechingly to the crowd to leave. When I walked out on to the street, Bill Sutton was standing talking to a group of men. As I came out he fell in beside me, the box on his shoulder.

'You're a battler, Mr Sutton, there's no doubt about you,' I remarked.

'Aw, cut out the Mr; call me Bill.'

'All right. And you call me Caddie.'

'Righto,' Bill said. 'Caddie! That's a bonzer name all right.'

The children were excited at the prospect of having a poultry dinner, and for Sunday I set the table as nicely as possible. We dined royally.

On the following Tuesday Bill called and I bought a rabbit off him. I had been worrying all the morning about the dole, and told Bill about the chief clerk seeing me in the bar.

Bill laughed, 'You needn't worry about 'im Caddie. 'E's a friend to all us doleys. Don't we all know it?'

'I'm not so sure.'

'Well, I am. I bet ya two bob he doesn't chat to yer about it. He's a white man, make no bloomer about that.'

Bill's assurances did little to still my fears, and I approached the dole office fearfully next issuing day. I took my place in the queue and waited to learn my fate. The clerk looked at me with a smile as he stamped my ration tickets, and I turned away with a sigh of relief. All that worry for nothing, I told myself, as I made my way down the street.

Looking through the *Herald* one morning I noticed an advertisement for a housekeeper from a man in the country. On the spur of the moment I sat down and answered it. The thought of going to the bush for a while appealed to me. It would be good for the children and fill my life while I was waiting for Peter.

A few days later I received a reply. It was from an orchardist, and he explained that he was a widower, with a grown-up family living in the district. He went on to say that he also ran a mixed farm and grew all his own food. He wrote that he was a respectable man and would provide us with a good home, the understanding being that I was to help in the orchard and about the farm when not doing house work. For these services he was prepared to pay me ten shillings per week.

At last we could get away from the slums, and I answered his letter accepting his offer. Already I could visualize Terry and Ann chasing rabbits, healthy and well fed.

When Bill called I told him about my good luck. He was

pleased, and said he hoped the bloke was fair dinkum. I said his letter sounded genuine.

'The ol' joker mightn't be all he's crackin' 'imself up ter be.'

'Well, he says he has a grown-up family living nearby,' I told him, and he seemed satisfied.

Counting my money I found that I would have just enough for our fares. Then I remembered that the rent was due next day. The landlady would be around next morning. I thought of selling the bed, and called in at the second-hand shop from where I had bought it. The man said he would come around and have a look at it, so I went home to wait.

When I turned into the street Bill Sutton was serving a woman with a rabbit, and gave me a cheery wave. I went inside and sat down, surveying our dismal luggage packed and ready near the front door. Bill found me, 'lookin' like I'd lorst a fiver and picked up sixpence', as he put it, when he came to the door, a rabbit in his hand.

'Hello, Bill,' I greeted him. 'I'm just waiting for the second-hand man to come and take the bed away.'

'Yer won't git much orf them blokes for it. But a few bob's better than nuthin', I suppose.'

'I got another letter from the orchardist this morning,' I told him. 'He'll meet us at the station on Sunday morning. I'm trying to figure out how I can get out of paying another week's rent here.'

'Hm. It's no good paying out good spondulicks if yer c'n help it.' Bill agreed.

'Well, sit down and I'll make you a cup of tea. Make our miserable lives happy,' I said cheerfully, and began putting the cups and saucers on the table. The table, I thought suddenly. Yes, I could sell that too, even if only for a few shillings.

As we sat drinking our tea, Bill looked at me, and exclaimed in self-disgust: 'What's wrong with me – where's me brains. Why, you can come round and doss at our place until you get yer train.'

'Your family mightn't like it, Bill. I'd be butting in.'

'Ya wouldn't be buttin' in. Don't be silly. Well, that's settled. We'll go around to my joint this afternoon, and yer c'n see the old lady fer yerself. Everythin's all right. I'll come for yer about four.'

He rose from the table. 'Thanks fer the tea. See you later. So long.'

Shortly after Bill had left, the second-hand man came.

'That's the bed, there,' I said unnecessarily, pointing to the only bed in the house.

'Hmm . . . ahhh . . . yes,' he meditated, rubbing his chin. 'I'll give you four shillin's for it,' he declared, after feeling the bed with a hairy fist

'All right, and I have a table outside.' I led the way to the kitchen.

He shook the table. 'Five an' six.'

'Five and six, and only four shillings for the bed?' I queried.

'More demand for tables than beds, Missus,' he said briefly, as he took a grubby purse from his hip pocket.

Counting out nine shillings and sixpence into my hand he said, 'I'll get me offsider. He's outside in the cart.'

He trotted outside, returning with a lad of about fourteen. They picked up the table and carried it out through the front door, then returned for the bed.

After they'd gone I sat down and surveyed the place. Except for the few boxes that had served as chairs, the place was as bare as the day I'd first walked into it.

Later in the afternoon Bill called, and we walked around to his home. The Sutton home was a large two-storied dwelling which stood well back from the street, and as we entered the gate, I noticed that their landlord had something in common with mine, for several of the windows were boarded over, and the whole place was shabby and in need of a coat of paint. Bill took me down the side path into the kitchen. There I met Mrs Sutton. She straightened up from the stove as we entered and turned to face me. She was a little, white-haired, softly-spoken old lady, and smiled a welcome as Bill introduced me.

Dadda Sutton came in from the front room. He looked years older than his wife, stooped, and shrunken-cheeked. He walked with a limp caused through a wound he received in the first war, but I found out later that what he may have lost in physical form was amply made up for by a fiery spirit absolutely unquenchable.

Mumma Sutton showed us up to the attic, informing me on the way that her boys did all the scrubbing in the house.

Entering the attic I thought how clean it was; but then, the whole house, although shabby, was scrupulously clean.

'Don't worry about your tea tonight, I think I can manage to give you enough for you and the kiddies, so come down as soon as you're ready,' said Mumma, as she left the room.

Some dispute as to the food was on when I returned later with the children.

Dadda Sutton was scowling across the table at the youngest son – Sonny he was called.

'Yer orta think yerself lucky ter 'ave it ter eat,' he said.

This seemed to infuriate Sonny. He pushed his plate aside and glared back at his father, who was finding it hard to masticate his food with his gums and talk at the same time.

Dadda went on, ignoring Sonny's scowl: 'A course ya lucky ter 'ave it ter eat. Yer ain't workin' are ya? Yer're on the dole like the rest of 'em.'

Sonny retorted, 'And whose fault is it that I'm on the dole? Did I want to leave school? No,' he answered himself, 'it was *you* who made me leave when I was halfway through the Inter.'

'I took yer away 'cause I 'ad no way o' keeping yer there. Any'ow, I kept yer long enough,' Dadda snapped.

'From school house to the dole house! Lovely, isn't it?' Sonny exclaimed.

'Turn it up,' Bill commanded. 'Yer can't beat the system, Sonny. Yer gotta make the best of it.'

'That may be your idea, Bill, but it isn't mine,' Sonny retorted. 'We could beat the system if we liked. We could beat the dole if we fought. All we've won in the past we've won by battling and only in struggle will we win anything in the future.'

38

Next morning I went around to the cottage from which I had moved the night before, to await the postman, for I expected a letter from Peter.

To my surprise he handed me two letters, one from Peter, and one from the orchardist. I put Peter's letter in my bag; turning the other one over and looking at it apprehensively I opened it slowly. It was from the orchardist all right, and was to say that he had consulted his family on the matter, and they felt that I was too young for the position, and that they had advised him to get a middle-aged woman. He hoped I hadn't been inconvenienced.

'So!' I groaned. Here I was in another jam. I'd sold my little home, given up my house, all for nothing. Once again I was on the outer. Apart from all that, I asked myself, how was I going to break it to the children, that they would not be going to the country after all. Besides, what would Dadda and Mumma Sutton say when they learned that they would still have us on their hands?

Miserably I turned in at the Sutton's gate and entered the house. Mumma Sutton was in the kitchen busily taking the jackets off some new potatoes. She looked up as I walked in, and I told her what had happened.

She gave me an encouraging smile. 'Never mind,' she said gently, 'I'm sure something will turn up for you. So don't let it worry you.'

I thanked her, for I was very glad that she did not seem to mind having us a little longer.

I then went upstairs to read Peter's letter, and think things out.

If I had hoped to get some measure of comfort from Peter's letter I was disappointed. Things had got much worse in Greece since he last wrote. His father's business was just tottering, and I could well imagine the struggle Peter was putting up in an effort to keep it going. There was no mention of his wife or divorce. It seemed hopeless that we would ever be able to settle down together. The future looked bleak indeed.

The children were out in the yard playing. When they came in I broke the news to them. They were both very disappointed, and Terry asked, 'What'll we do now, Mummie?'

I felt depressed, but made light of the situation. I thought I'd better let Bill see the letter I had got from the orchardist, and went looking for him. I found him over near the stable door. He was sitting intently studying a racing form guide. I handed him the letter.

'Well, I reckon yer like me. If it was rainin' soup we'd 'ave a fork.'

Last night, I thought, I'd been looking forward to getting away from all this poverty, and now found myself worse off than ever.

I went back to the hotel that afternoon wondering as I entered the bar whether I would be able to cancel my notice. When I got an opportunity I went over to the Missus who was sitting at the till and asked her if I might keep my job, explaining the position to her. She assured me it would be all right as she'd not made any arrangement to get someone in my place.

Well, that's one consolation, I told myself, as I made my way home after work. I knew how hard it was then to get a job of any kind, and considered myself lucky.

The city sweltered under one of the worst heatwaves on record. The bar was crowded. Men drank and talked in desultory tones as the temperature rose steadily. Bill came in and pushing his way through the crowd breasted the bar. Tilting his hat on to the back of his head he greeted me with: 'Ain't it a corker?'

I nodded, asking, 'What'll you have, Bill?'

'Better make it a pint.'

He put six pennies on the counter, and when I returned with his drink he was searching his pockets for the extra threepence he knew he didn't have.

'Blimey, I'm sure I 'ad another trizzy somewhere,' he frowned and made a great show of going through his pockets. A man near him, seeing his plight, tossed threepence on to the pile of coppers. Bill looked up in feigned surprise, saying: 'Thanks, mate!'

He spat at his feet, saying, 'Cripes, it takes a man all 'is time ter raise a spit. 'Ere's mud in yer eye,' and winking at me, he raised the glass to his lips.

The night was still hot. I sent the children upstairs to get ready for bed, telling them that I was going over to the shop and would have a surprise for them when I came back. A customer had given me a shilling tip that afternoon, so I thought I'd give them a treat. I bought an ice-cream for each of them, and some bread and two eggs with the change. When I entered the attic, Terry and Ann were sitting bolt upright in bed, a look of expectancy on their faces. Handing them the ice-cream I sat on the bed beside them.

Terry said, 'Gee, you are a good mother – isn't she, Ann?'

To which Ann nodded, intent upon her ice-cream.

'I hope you'll always think so, and some day, when you're a man, and have lots of money, you won't forget to come and see me when I am old and living in a little room in some back street.'

'Listen, Mum, the only little room you'll have then will be your bathroom; 'cause when I grow up I'm going to be a arcateck, and I'm going to draw a lovely house for you, and have it built for you. A lovely place with mirrors and cream things all around your bathroom walls,' he said almost in one breath.

Ann chimed in with: 'Yes, and I'm going to buy you lovely hats and jewels and things, Mummie.'

'My goodness me! Why, I'm going to be the luckiest mother in Australia,' I exclaimed.

'In the world!' corrected Terry.

I had a lump in my throat as I hugged them.

Mumma Sutton gave me the impression that she'd long since given up under the strain of Dadda Sutton's aggressive nature and the constant battle against poverty and want. She went about her daily work quietly and uncomplainingly.

Bill adored his mother, so did Sonny. It seemed they tolerated their father and tried to keep the peace as much as possible for her sake. Whenever Bill had a stroke of luck like backing a winner, or getting a few extra shillings, he'd share it with his mother, on the understanding that she'd spend it on herself. But very often the money would find its way on to the table for a little extra food.

Mumma Sutton was confined to her room for a few days, and it fell to Bill to take over the duties in the kitchen. It was the day before dole day, and there was very little to eat in the house. I went to the kitchen where Bill was pottering about, and looking into cupboards and peering into tins in the hope of finding enough to make up an evening meal. He scratched his head as I walked in, saying something about there not being a crumb in the cupboard, and that he couldn't even find anything to pawn either.

'Me clobber's already in Moscow, an' so is me tan shoes. I'm blowed if I know, but there don't seem nuthin' a man can raise a deaner on.'

I didn't know what to say, for I, too, was broke. I tried to think if I had anything worth pawning, but there was nothing I could think of. I had nothing of any value except my sewing-machine. I just couldn't run the risk of pawning that. I'd probably never be able to redeem it. Then I thought of the Bible, and said, 'All I've got is a Bible. If you think you could raise a few shillings on it, you're welcome.'

'Good-o! Thanks,' he said.

I went upstairs and returned with the Bible. I told him it would be all right as long as he didn't let the interest lapse on it. He assured me it would be O.K. and that he'd get it out again at the week-end.

Bill set off to the little pawn shop on Main Street. He wrapped the Bible carefully, saying, 'A man doesn't want anyone to see 'im carrying a Bible. Might think he's a sky pilot.'

As I was preparing to go to work I found Bill busily engaged in the kitchen, chopping stewing steak into small pieces for a stew. He seemed in a quandary as to what he could put in with the meat, as he'd only got two and sixpence on the Bible. After buying the meat and spuds, and a loaf of bread he found he didn't have enough to buy vegetables to put in the stew. Inquiring hopelessly if I had an onion, he went out into the backyard, and I was astonished to see him cut some grass, wash it, then chop it up and add it to the saucepan of meat.

He laughed at my astonishment and said, 'They won't be any the wiser when they eat it. Any'ow 'oo was the politician wot said the workers could go and eat grass?'*

I replied that I hadn't heard that one, and he said, 'Yeah, someone said it all right, an' now 'is words is gonna come true.'

He whistled cheerfully as he placed the pot on the stove.

Tea-time came and we were all seated around the table while Bill began to dish out the stew just as Pat, the younger daughter came rushing in from work. Everything seemed to be going fine when Dadda Sutton began grizzling.

Bill looked up as Dadda made some derogatory remark about the tucker.

'If it's upter why don't you 'ave a go? Strike me lucky! A man tries ter do 'is best, an' wot 'appens?' Bill asked with growing indignation.

'Yer old enough ter be able ter cook better than this, ain't yer?' Dadda asked disagreeably.

'Yeah, per'aps I am. But why should I have ter do all the graft about the place while you set around moanin'. I'm only doin' it 'cause the old lady's crook,' he reminded Dadda, and added, 'You can try yerself out termorrer an' see 'ow you go.'

'Yer don't think I'm goin' ter do it? I've 'ad my day,' grumbled the old man.

'Of course y've 'ad yer day . . . everyone knows that,' Bill answered sarcastically.

*In a period of stress and strikes an Australian politician was alleged to have made that remark.

'Too right,' Pat agreed, tasting the stew. 'What did you make it of, Bill? Old boots and seaweed?'

'It tastes all right to me,' said Sonny as he chased a fragment of meat with a crust of bread.

'Blimey, that's a break,' Bill answered as he sat down and began eating.

After he had taken a few mouthfuls he said, 'I don't see nuthin' ter bellyache about it. Tastes O.K.'

Bill was the brains of the family as far as battling was concerned, and obtained three issues on dole days. He did this by registering at three different dole depots under three different names. As the various depots issued at the same time, Bill solved the problem by borrowing a cobber's push bike, with which he was able to cover the ground. He sold two of the tickets for ready cash, and handed the other to Mumma Sutton. So, with his rabbit-run, dwindling though it was, and his dole tickets he managed to get along. 'And while there's anything in the Sutton cupboard, Caddie,' he assured me when I said I couldn't stay and pole on them, 'it's yours.'

That was Bill Sutton!

39

I didn't feel so bad about poling on them when I found I could be a great help to them all since Mumma Sutton never got up again and there was a lot to do looking after her and doing the jobs she had always done.

She was a sweet and gentle creature, grateful for everything one did. And in some way, as she got weaker, she confused Ann and Terry with her own children as they had been twenty years before.

Sonny and I became firm friends. In the evenings he would sometimes come upstairs and sit on the top stair playing his mouth-organ and talking to me. One could not help liking this earnest young man.

Once he said: 'You know, somehow I like talking to you; you seem to understand a bloke. The family don't seem interested.'

He told me how he wanted dearly to become a doctor, and how unhappy he had been when his father insisted upon him leaving school to take a job he couldn't get. The depression was well under way then. He told me how he had walked the city from one end to the other in search of work, but everywhere found signs saying: 'No hands required.'

Dadda Sutton, crotchety, aggressive, always grumbling, seemed to rely on me too. At first he couldn't understand that Mumma was ill: 'Never had a day's sickness in her life,' he boasted. 'Up a coupla days after the kids was born.' He'd hover round the door anxiously while I washed her and made her bed. 'Real nice day outside, Mumma,' he'd plead. 'You orter get up. Do you good.'

And Mumma would say meekly, as she'd said all her life, 'Yes, Dadda,' and look at him with faded anxious eyes.

After several months she died as she had lived, quietly and unobtrusively.

The strain of looking after her and the family, as well as going to my job every afternoon, had its effect on me. I continued to lose weight and was always tired. Then added to this, the Missus at the pub told me that because business wasn't too brisk on weekdays I would only be required to come to work on Friday and Saturday afternoons. That she would have the cook and housemaid come in the bar in my place explaining that she must cut down on expenditure. This meant that I would only get about a quarter of my usual pay.

I think this must have put the finishing touches to my already poor state of health. While waiting to be served at the counter of Mrs Prinnter's shop across the street from the Suttons, I became dizzy and, without warning, I fainted.

When Mrs Prinnter had reluctantly let me leave the shop I walked slowly across the street thinking to myself: I mustn't allow myself to become sick; that would never do. For one thing I couldn't afford to be sick. My children needed me. Besides, I was afraid that if I couldn't care for them the Welfare Department might take them away from me. I'd take Mrs Prinnter's advice and try to take more care of myself. But that wouldn't be easy, for I knew that what I needed most was more food and better living conditions. Which was all very well, but how was I going to alter things?

I fainted again just as I got inside the door. Hours later, it seemed, I lay back on the pillows watching Ann as she moved quietly around the room. She was putting things away and straightening the bedclothes, for Bill had just gone to fetch Doctor Dewey.

When Bill had first mentioned going for the doctor I protested that I didn't need a doctor, that I would be all right in a day or two. But Bill was firm about it, saying, 'Blimey, don't be silly. Why, ye've looked crook fer weeks now, an' don't look like yer gettin' orlright.'

Doctor Dewey came. He looked at me over his glasses as he put his hat and bag on a chair, then sat down beside me on the edge of the bed. He took my wrist and felt for my pulse, and asked the usual questions, then began writing out a prescription.

He told me that I was suffering from malnutrition and nervous exhaustion. I was to take the tonic he had prescribed, improve my diet, and have plenty of rest. I mumbled something about paying his bill but he just smiled and said, 'We'll forget about that.'

After he had gone Bill came in, followed closely by Ann.

'Well,' said Bill, 'wot did the quack 'ave ter say?'

I told him, and showed him the prescription saying, 'I won't be able to get it made up; haven't got the money, Bill.'

He thought for a moment, then said: 'Look 'ere, I won't be likely ter be gettin' mokkered up before Satadey, so I'll pop me clobber termorrer ter raise the wind for yer.'

I knew it was no good protesting, so I said, 'You're very good to me, Bill.'

'Aw, cut it out! Good, be blowed!' he said scornfully.

Ann, who had been taking all this in, her eyes never leaving Bill's face for a second, said emphatically, 'You are so, Bill Sutton, so there!'

When I found that I couldn't carry on any longer, Bill took over for me. He gave the children their meals, and saw that they got away to school on time each morning. He used to bring me my meals, and sometimes Pat or Sonny would take it in turns to bring me my evening meal.

Bill usually went out at night for a game of cards, or sometimes he would play two-up in the back lane with some of the neighbours. Pat and Sonny would sometimes come up to the attic and spend a couple of hours with me. Once Dadda Sutton came for a few minutes.

For all their kindness I fretted about the children, and wondered how much grass they consumed whenever Bill decided to concoct one of his grass-stew specials. Apparently it didn't do them any harm.

When dole day came around, I gave Bill a note authorizing

him to collect my dole ration. He came in looking very pleased with himself saying, 'Well, I landed an extra fortnight's ration for yer.'

'However did you manage that?' I asked quickly.

'Aw, 'ow do yer think I managed it?' he said as he handed me the tickets.

'You didn't work a swiftie on them, did you?' I asked suspiciously. For I was already aware that Bill was collecting three doles for himself.

'No, I didn't work no swiftie. I'm surprised at you! I saw the king pin . . . didn't I tell yer 'e was a white man?'

I looked at him inquiringly.

'Yeah, I drummed him about you bein' crook. Told him what the Doc said. That did the trick.'

'There's no doubt about you, Bill, you're a good scout,' I said, on the verge of tears with gratitude.

Several weeks had passed since Bill had brought home the double issue of dole tickets. I was feeling much better, and was beginning to think about getting back to work.

One evening Bill came home looking more pleased than ever. 'I got a big surprise for yer,' he said, grinning broadly.

'Well, tell me the worst.'

He came over and stood beside the bed. 'There y'are,' he said, dropping a handful of bank-notes on the bed beside me.

'For heaven's sake! Where did you get them?' I exclaimed.

'They're all yours, every one of 'em. Gorn! Count 'em.'

I just stared at him.

'Gorn! Count 'em.'

I obeyed, my hands trembling a little.

'Yer got a spin,' he said, as I picked up a five-pound note. 'An' four greenbacks. Yer get nine quid in all.'

'But where did it all come from, Bill,' I asked mystified.

'It was like this. I wus round at the pub, an' some bloke took the 'at around.'

'You mean they collected this for me from the customers?'

'Yeah, o' course.'

I stared at the money. I don't think I've ever felt so humiliated in my life. Stupid perhaps, but all my mother's pride rose up and nearly choked me. I wondered what Peter would think.

'I don't know whether I should keep it,' I said reluctantly.

'Gawd blimey! Don't think yer orta keep it! Is that all the thanks a man gits fer tryin' to pull yer out of the soup?'

knew then that Bill had organized the collection. He had

taken the hat around the bar, asking the customers to help me.
I might have known. But I still had that stupid pride. Besides,
I knew how hard-up most of our customers were. Not many
of them could afford more than a daily half-pint nowadays.
I thought of them forking out their hard-earned treys and
zacks and bobs and nearly cried.

'But isn't that cadging?'

'Break it down,' he answered sharply. 'It only shows that
yer customers appreciate yer, that's all.'

I thought it over for a while, then said slowly: 'You know,
Bill, you're full of surprises. Every day I learn something more
about you. I've never met anyone quite like you before.'

'Aw, cut the comedy,' he said full of embarrassment and
walked out.

40

When I was back on my feet again I decided that the best
thing for me to do was to try to find a house again. I could
never be grateful enough to the Suttons but I wanted a home
for my children that was a home, no matter how poor, and
I wanted to rear them my way, not Dadda Sutton's. He had
got more and more difficult since Mumma's death and never a
day passed without a row, particularly between Pat and her
father. It began to get on my nerves.

Bill sympathized with my desire – I think they understood
what was in my mind though it was never put into words. In
his usual generous way Bill started house-hunting for me and
at last came home with the good news that he had found an
empty cottage and had inquired at the agent's for me. I went
along to this man and had no difficulty in getting the place,
for I was able to show him all my rent receipts which I had
collected from Dadda Sutton.

We moved in. It was damp and cheerless, for the sun
couldn't reach round the factories surrounding it on all sides.
But it was home anyway. I began to settle in, feeling more
enthusiastic than I'd felt for a very long time. Somehow,
having our own place again made me feel closer to Peter and
when the day we moved in a letter arrived from him, it made
the illusion more real.

The very first thing was to have the gas and electricity connected. I went to the Gas Company, and was surprised to see one of my old customers from saloon bar days. I went over to him at once. He was sitting on a high stool at the counter, his head bent over some documents. He looked up as I spoke and smiled.

'Hullo! What brings you here?'

'I've come to see about having the gas connected.'

'Right!'

He reached under the counter for a form; then began asking me particulars, stopping every now and then in his writing to ask me how I was, and where I worked. I told him.

'What's the beer like there?' he asked.

'It's pretty good,' I replied, adding that, according to some of my customers, all beer was good.

'Did you say you were the owner of the premises?' he asked.

I laughed. 'I wish you meant it! Unfortunately I'm only the tenant.'

He leant over the counter. 'Couldn't you *be* the owner?'

I looked at him, puzzled.

'If you happen to be the owner you don't have to pay any deposit.'

Light dawned on me. 'I catch on,' I said. 'But wouldn't I get into trouble for making a false statement?'

'Who the hell's to know as long as you don't tell your neighbours and keep the account paid.'

With that, he tore up the form he had been filling in and took another, and signed me up as the owner.

'I suppose you want it on by tonight?' he said, glancing at the big clock on the wall. It was then two-thirty.

Although I hadn't expected to have it on that soon, I said: 'Well, yes, if possible.'

'Wait a minute,' he said, lifting the receiver off the hook, 'I'll give my mate a tinkle.'

He spoke into the phone. I heard him say, 'That you, Long'un? Got a job I want you to do. What's that? Too late? But it's for a friend of mine. You will? O.K. Thanks, mate.'

He hung up.

He assured me that he'd fixed it so that I'd have the gas on that afternoon.

'Thanks a lot. That's terribly good of you.'

166

'Not at all. We slaves have to stick together you know.'

'Slaves?' I laughed, thinking that compared with my job, pen-pushing would be a push-over and I told him so.

He chuckled. 'That's what *you* think.'

As I turned to go he called after me. 'I'll be over your way on Saturday afternoon to sample the beer, and look out for yourself if it isn't as good as you reckon it is.'

I went straight from there to the County Council to see about having the electricity connected. But I didn't meet any one there that I knew so had to wait my turn. I kind of hoped I would, though.

From there I went to see the solicitor who was making the necessary arrangements for my divorce. Things were going well, he told me. They had succeeded in serving papers on John, who was apparently back living with his mother and was not going to defend the suit. I came out thinking that evidently my mother-in-law had won after all. I wondered what had become of Esther.

I returned home, feeling quite cheerful, just in time to see Long'un getting up from the meter on my verandah.

'Is it on?' I asked in surprise.

He nodded and told me to try the stove.

I opened the front door and went into the kitchen. 'Yes, it's on. That was quick work, all right.'

'Yeah, that's the best of having good pals.'

In our second home, we were in much the same position as before, with a box which served as a cupboard for keeping food and crockery, and fruit cases for chairs.

From the nine pounds which Bill had collected for me I bought another second-hand bed and a small table for the kitchen.

When the weather was not too cold at night we would sit up until about nine o'clock, Terry getting out his drawing gear, and Ann making clothes for her dolls – those that Peter had bought for her.

A few days after moving in, I was in the bar when the Missus said, 'Hop out to the kitchen and make a cup of tea.'

I was feeling like a cup myself and went to the kitchen and put the kettle on the gas. The cook-general was out in the laundry washing. I took a cup out to her first. As I arrived back in the kitchen the boss walked in and said in a whisper, 'There's a bloke in the bar wants to see you.'

'Who is he?' I asked fearfully.

'I dunno, but if you ask me he's got departmental written all over him.'

'Not a copper?' I felt myself grow cold.

'No, I don't think so. He's in civvies.'

By this time I had the tray ready, and set forth for the bar.

As I came into the bar I spotted the man at the same time as he spotted me. He was the only stranger in the bar.

As I set the tray down alongside the Missus, she nodded in the stranger's direction and said, 'That gent wants to see you.'

He watched me as I walked over. 'Are you Mrs Marsh?'

I replied that I was.

'I'm from the Child Welfare Department; I'm an investigation officer.'

'Oh!' I said. I hope I didn't look as nervous as I felt. 'Will you come around here, please?'

I walked to the parlour door, opened it for him to enter, and showed him to a table.

'Excuse me,' I said as I whisked two empty beer glasses off and took them out to the bar.

He got down to business. 'The Department has been informed that you are working and that you have not stated your income correctly. What have you to say to that, Mrs Marsh?'

To myself I said, 'What dirty swine has potted me?' Aloud I remarked calmly: 'Me working? I wish I was.'

He gave me a I'm-not-as-silly-as-I-look glance and said: 'What were you doing when I arrived?'

'I just give them a hand here occasionally, that's all.' I hoped I wouldn't get the shakes.

He leaned across the table and stared intently into my face. 'Do you mean to tell me you're not in receipt of wages?'

His tone made me wonder just how much he *did* know.

'That's right. They're friends of mine. They're very good to me. They give me their left-off clothing, and often take the children to the pictures.'

This was not the truth, but the boss did give me the complimentary picture tickets he received for allowing the local picture show to exhibit their bills in his bar and on the walls outside.

I decided to kid silly. 'It's true,' I affirmed, with what I hoped was a not-too-vacuous expression on my face. 'You can ask them yourself if you like.'

He went on writing, making no answer.

I tried to figure out what sort of an impression I had made. 'Who told you I was working?' I asked.

He ignored the question and merely continued with his writing.

I was worried for fear someone would come into the parlour and unwittingly blow the gaff. It was unusual for it to be empty at this time of the day. Sure enough, a couple tried to enter. I hurried to the door. It was one of our regulars looking for somewhere to have a quiet spot with his lady friend.

'Not in here, if you don't mind, Barnsey. In the other parlour, please.'

Barnsey said, 'Righto, Caddie,' and the door closed.

When the officer had finished writing he placed the papers back in his attaché case and rose to go. 'You'll be hearing from the Department in a few days,' was his parting comment.

I went back to the bar. He had not questioned my employers. Did he believe me, I wondered?

The Missus had just finished serving a customer. Tossing the money into the till, she climbed back on to her stool behind the cash-register. 'Better drink your tea,' she said.

I didn't want the tea now, and anyway it was cold. I felt so worried I thought a stiff brandy would be more like it.

'What did he say?' she asked.

'He said the Department had received information that I was working and hadn't stated my income correctly,' I whispered.

The lone customer sipped his beer, rolled a smoke, staring at us and probably wondering what the muttering was about.

The Missus, eyeing the customer with suspicion, whispered: 'Have you ever seen *him* before?'

I took a good look at the man and shook my head.

'It might be a trap. He might've been sent here to catch you in the act of serving behind the bar.'

Just then the man, having drained his glass, banged it down on the counter, a signal that he wanted another drink. The Missus struggled with her thirteen stone to get down from the stool, but the man called out, 'Stay where y'are, Ma, I'll have the young lady to serve me, if you don't mind.'

There was nothing unusual about this request, as lots of customers liked a barman or barmaid to serve them in preference to the bosses, but I, too, had become suspicious that this was a trap all right.

The Missus made some remark about me not being too well. 'She looks all right ter me,' he said.

I felt it was time I wasn't there, and hurried out to the kitchen. The cook-laundress had finished the washing and was busily preparing the meal. I continued on to the laundry.

The boss was busy at the tubs washing rum bottles, and not liking it very much. The useful, whose job it was, had been fired the night before. I told him what had happened. He merely grunted, and said, 'You'd better lie low for a while until it blows over.'

I knew we couldn't exist on Government aid without the few extra shillings I earned, and I couldn't support my little family on my pay. So I decided to stick to my job and take the risk. I didn't want to put it over the Government, but just wanted enough to feed and clothe my children decently.

When the day arrived on which I usually received the cheque from the Welfare Department, I waited anxiously at the gate for the postman. He came along, gay as usual, but shook his head slowly. There was no letter for me. The posty stopped for a chat, and I told him what had happened, and my fears about the Department stopping the cheque.

I said: 'Someone must have potted me.'

He looked at me quizzically: 'Don't you know who told them?'

'I haven't the faintest.'

He turned his head on one side, and looked at me with mock impatience. 'Your neighbours, Missus. That's who does it . . . your neighbours.'

I couldn't believe it. 'But they're all in the same boat.'

'Yeah, I know, but p'raps you're getting a bit more than them. You mightn't believe me, but I've had people pull me up in the street and say, "Does Mrs So and So get Government letters?"'

'No!'

'Of course, I don't give 'em any information. Even if I was low enough it'd be more than me job's worth.'

'Well, there's no doubt about some of them,' I said disgustedly.

'Ah well, I suppose I'd better be on my way,' he said, and walked on, giving his heavy bag a hitch as he went.

41

Remembering the advice of Mrs Yardley at the dole office, I decided to go and see the local Member. I'd have to fight to get this money back. It seemed he was my only hope. His home was not very far from where I lived, but was on the better side of the suburb. It was a beautiful house situated in a wide street; it's smooth sidewalks were lined with trees.

Arriving, I walked along the garden path to the front door which was standing open, a blaze of light from the verandah lighting up the front of the house and garden. As I came self-consciously to the door I could see into a large room in which a number of people had already gathered. Obviously this was one of the nights set aside by the Member for the convenience of his constituents. I was in luck, I thought, as I reached for the door-bell. A pleasant woman came forward from a room at the end of the wide hall. I explained that I wished to see the Member. She smiled as she asked me to come in, with a flourish of a hand that glittered with precious stones. I took a seat, hoping I wouldn't have too long to wait as I'd left the children at home.

I looked around the room, and assumed that this was where the Member and his family took their first meal of the day. A door led from here to the kitchen which, I saw, when the door was opened, was large and very modern. Neat built-in cupboards painted in cream and green lined one wall. An elaborate refrigerator throbbed importantly beside a gleaming sink.

After about half an hour it was my turn to go in and interview the Member. He was seated at a desk in what appeared to be a study. He smiled and offered me a seat.

I explained my position as he examined the tip of his pencil. I told him that I was getting Government assistance, and that the Welfare Department had stopped payments to me, and I thought that it was because an officer of that Department had found me working. I told him that I had been earning a few shillings, that it was impossible for me to manage on the help I was receiving from the Government, and I was forced to earn a little extra to keep things going.

He jotted down the particulars on a pad before him, telling me that he would get in touch with the head of the Department next morning. With that I got up.

He said, 'I'll see what I can do for you.'

I thank him and went out. As I left the room the large lady showed the next caller in.

Next morning I was standing at the front gate waving to the children as they made their way up the street to school, when a large sedan drew up in front of the house. It was the Member. What an unearthly hour to call, I thought, thinking of the untidy house behind me. Besides it did not seem necessary for him to call on me as I was sure that I had given him all the particulars of my case the night before. He stepped from his car and slammed the door with a flourish. I ushered him into the house. He was dressed in a warm-looking overcoat, and wore a black hard hitter – quite the popular idea of what a politician should look like.

I indicated one of the boxes. He placed his hard hitter on the mantelpiece, and removed his fur-lined gloves. He showed the usual caution of all my visitors when accepting a fruit case to sit on. Finding it withstood his weight he relaxed and looked about the room and up at the blackened ceiling. 'This is a terrible state of affairs. Er – what help did you say you were getting from the Government?'

I explained again that I'd been in receipt of one pound from the Child Welfare Department, and food relief for the three of us. He shook his head.

'It's impossible to get even the bare necessities with that small amount.'

He drew out his fountain pen and notebook, balancing the book on his knee as he wrote.

When he'd finished he rose, slipped the book into his overcoat pocket and moved over to the hearth. The fire I had made with rubbish from the backyard to warm the children as they ate their breakfast was still burning in the grate. As he leaned against the mantelpiece, his watch chain and gold pass could be seen through his unbuttoned coat. He spread his hands out in front of the fire and briskly rubbed the chill from them as he spoke.

'It is an awful thing that you have to live like this. I can't

172

understand how a man could leave you in that way; in fact, I can't imagine how a man could leave *you* at all. He must have been mad . . . it's beyond me.'

Although no woman finds flattery hard to take I was embarrassed. This was hardly the time and place for it. Being a wake-up to men by now, I was on the alert at once.

'You know,' he said, 'I could do a lot for you, if you'd only say the word.'

There was no mistaking his meaning. Right then, I wanted to smack the smug look off his face, but remembered my need of Government assistance, and said calmly:

'I am afraid I don't know what you mean.'

My manner gave him his answer. He understood. He'd made a mistake.

He laughed: 'You've nothing to be afraid of. I've always been a gentleman and I wish to remain one.'

My empty stomach rolled over and I trembled.

He said: 'Why, you're cold!'

I felt awkward and foolish, and answered, 'I *am* a little cold.'

He took out his wallet and held out a pound note towards me.

I made no attempt to take it. He smiled and placed it on the mantelpiece with that same smug look on his face.

I was inwardly furious, as it seemed the money was meant as compensation for the insult.

Pulling on his gloves he walked towards the door, assuring me as he went that he would do his best for me in contacting the Department about the money owing to me. I hurried forward to open the door for him. He bade me good-day and walked out to his car, once more the business-like politician.

As he drove away, Mrs Morley, who was sweeping her front verandah across the street, called out: 'Gittin' 'igh up in the world ain't yer?'

I merely smiled back at her. One couldn't afford to snub one's neighbour in this district. I looked into the letter box then went inside. Hurriedly I went to the mantelpiece. No need to worry about the rent this week, I thought, as I picked up the pound. And now for some breakfast. I went across to the little shop on the corner and spent a corner of the pound on food for the day, and rolled the rest of the silver in the ten shilling note very carefully and put it away for the rent.

That's how it was – scratching all the time to make ends meet.

Within a few days I received a cheque for the full amount owing, also a letter from the Department regretting the delay in forwarding same. There was no mention of why the money had been stopped, so I presumed the politician had taken care of that.

42

Three years went by and I seemed no nearer realizing my hopes of a real home and security. Peter's letters continued but he began to sound so sad and depressed in them that I used to try to cheer him up by writing long letters telling him all about the children and what we were doing. I'm afraid they weren't strictly honest letters. I hadn't the heart to tell him what was really happening and how really badly off we were.

I don't know what I'd have done at times only for the Suttons who became a kind of second family to me.

I was beginning to think I would never be able to lift myself out of this poverty that snowed us under, when one afternoon a police car turned the corner of my street. It stopped before a ramshackle cottage opposite my home. This was where a vicious old scandalmonger named Sarah Tunks lived. She'd been taking bets on commission for some bookie.

Almost before the car had stopped, two policeman jumped out and ran into Sarah's place. From where I was sitting I couldn't see what was happening. Then the two policemen reappeared escorting Sarah, one of them carrying slips of paper – betting slips, I guessed. She was dressed in an old, faded blue rig-out and was wearing red felt slippers. She protested loudly as one of the officers took her arm and pushed her into the car.

I watched the car disappear down the street.

A knot of people gathered around the cottage, peering with morbid curiosity at the scene of the crime. My next-door neighbour, watching from her front gate, called to me. 'Looks like a bit of bother fer old Sarah; second time she's gorn orf. Looks like she'll 'ave ter take it out if Paddy don't pay 'er fine.'

Paddy, I took it, was the big bookie for whom Sarah did the betting.

'Any'ow, I 'ope they give 'er six months without the option – it'll keep 'er tongue quiet fer a while.'

I went inside without answering.

A few days later a knock came to my door. Opened, it revealed a little fat man in a well-cut suit with high cheekbones and shamrocks in his eyes. He swung round from his examination of the street to face me, his plump little hands on his hips.

He raised his hat. 'Good afternoon. You're Mrs Marsh?' he stated rather than asked.

I agreed that I was Mrs Marsh.

'I'm Paddy Maher.'

So *this* is Paddy Maher? I thought.

He came straight to the point: 'How would you like to take over the bettin' for me in the pub and around this district?'

'Why come to me?' I asked cautiously.

'The Missus up at the pub told me about you. Said you might like to make a bit of extra money. She recommended you to me; said you were a straight goer.'

'That was nice of her.'

'If you take it on I'll give you one and six in the pound and pay your fine *if* you go off; or two shillings in the pound, and you pay your own fine . . . if any.'

'I'll let you know in a day or two,' I said thoughtfully.

'Right!' he said briskly, handing me a piece of paper on which was written his phone number. With that he went back to his car which was parked in front of my gate.

Although I'd told him I'd think it over and let him know in a day or two, I knew then that I would accept his offer.

I was well aware of the risk I'd be taking, but most of my neighbours took risks at sometime or other, I thought, and got away with it. Why not me? I decided to hang on to Government assistance while I could. I was determined that my children would have full stomachs and decent clothing, and hang the consequences.

So I began my new role as S.P. bookie. I thought I'd have to give up my job but soon found that the Missus was only too anxious to have one of her staff as the pub S.P. as it attracted custom. I used to take bets in the bar for the Wednesday and Saturday race meetings. Of course, there was always the danger of someone squealing on me to the police but I think he'd have been lynched in that bar. Besides, I used to put the betting slips in the leg of my bloomers and trusted to be able to make a getaway to the 'Ladies' with the evidence if the police ever raided me.

Paddy used to come round to my place in the evening after the races and next day I'd settle with the winners.

I became well known in the neighbourhood in my new role and, I believe, well liked, except for a few who had nothing better to do than pot people who seemed to be a little better off than themselves. I heard the remarks that were passed at times, such as, ' 'Ow does she manage ter doll up like she does on wot she gits?' and, 'Yer carn't tell me!' These I ignored, as I didn't doll up, but dressed very simply while still trying to take a pride in my appearance. When we were penniless none of the critics offered to help, so they were the least of my worries.

I began to have fewer headaches about money, and we had something approaching a home, and enough to eat.

After a few weeks I'd saved five pounds out of the proceeds of my betting business, and the outlook seemed good for a continuance so I went to a firm of house furnishers to get furniture on time-payment. I decided to buy the furniture for three rooms for fifty pounds, including floor coverings. It was pretty poor stuff, of course, but magnificent besides fruit cases and butter boxes. The salesman invited me into a tiny office. Seating himself at his desk he began drawing up the hire purchase agreement.

I'd tried before to get a cash order for clothing, and been informed that because I didn't have a husband they couldn't do business with me. At last the contract was almost complete. He asked the name of my husband, his occupation, and where he worked. I took another risk. Giving the name of Smith, I said my husband's name was William, and that he worked on the Government railways. Surely there would be hundreds of Smiths working on the railway, I thought.

He asked me for the deposit, which I gave him.

'The weekly instalment is seven and sixpence,' he explained as he pushed the document over for me to sign. He handed me a pen, and I scratched my signature at the spot where he had made a mark.

'Take it home and get your husband to sign on the top line; as soon as we receive it back we'll send the goods out to you.'

'Let me see,' he said as he looked at a book beside him. 'It's Monday; our carrier does your district Fridays, so if you get that contract back to us in the next day or so, you will get the goods on Friday.'

On the way home I wondered how I was going to get a mythical husband to sign the contract. Then I thought of Bill Sutton. I'd ask him what to do; he'd know. Bill clothed himself on cash orders, using the money he got for dole tickets.

When I showed Bill the contract and told him what the salesman had said, he said: 'Show me the paper wot's got ter be signed.' I handed it to him, and he said, 'Half a mo. Wait till I put me winkers on.' Reaching into his pocket he pulled out a pair of metal rimmed glasses. He studied the paper for a few minutes, then said, 'Wot's. wrong with me signin' it for yer?'

'Could you do that?'

'Wot's ter stop me? Here, give me a pen.'

I watched as he signed the name of William Smith.

'There!' He straightened up. 'Wot's wrong with that?'

I looked at the signature. It looked as though it had been written with a finger nail dipped in ink. That was Bill, rough and ready, but with a heart of gold.

When I told the children we would be getting some new furniture they were delighted, and begged to be allowed to stay at home from school on Friday. I told them they could, if they promised to help me; they both promised, and Ann wanted to know if she could have the permanent job of dusting the tables and chairs.

That Friday was a red-letter day. The furniture arrived before lunch time, and the event didn't pass unnoticed by the neighbours. Things were looking up in the Marsh home.

Bill Sutton came around and laid the linos. He arrived with a sharp knife and a hammer in his belt and set to work.

Terry said, 'We can leave the front door open now, Mum. It doesn't matter if people do see inside now that we have lino on our floors.'

Sonny arrived later. I was standing on a chair arranging the curtains on the dining-room window. I had a mouthful of tacks and had Bill's hammer in my hand when Sonny strode over and ordered me to get down. Jumping to the floor, I said: 'That suits me.' I felt so happy, I wouldn't have changed places with anyone. That night I sat down and wrote a long letter to Peter and I'm sure when he got it he must have imagined we were living in a mansion. When you've got little, it takes very little to make you happy.

43

On the strength of my new job, I bought Sonny a pair of shoes, because I had noticed when last he had been around that the ones he was wearing were almost hanging off his feet. Boots were the worst problem when you were on the dole for a long time.

My next problem was how to get Sonny to accept them. One had to be careful about offering him anything, because he was very touchy about such things.

Next night he came, the shoes were placed right where he couldn't help but see them.

'Who owns the shoes?' he asked, and bent his head to examine them closely.

'A customer left them at the pub. They were under the counter for months, so I claimed them.' I lied beautifully, I thought. I continued, 'I came across them today.'

Sonny picked one up. 'Gee, they're a nice pair of shoes all right.'

'Not bad.'

Sonny turned the shoes over. 'They're my size, too.'

'If they're your size, you had better take them.'

'Yes, but . . .' he started to say.

I interrupted him, knowing that he was about to refuse.

'You wouldn't expect me to wear them, would you?' I asked.

'Perhaps I could manage to pay you something off them each week,' he suggested.

'Whatever for? They cost me nothing.'

I decided that I should have been an actress. I watched him as he inspected them again. I knew he was trying to work out how he could pay for them, so I said, 'Listen, Sonny, take the damn things out of my sight!'

'All right. Thanks. But I've still got to pay you something for them, somehow.'

I changed the subject by suggesting we have a game of cards. He agreed, and sitting down began shuffling the cards from a pack he had brought with him.

But I wasn't too happy about Sonny, as his visits dropped off altogether without any warning. One night Pat came round to see me and to tell me she had lost her job. There'd been a row at the factory. An election was coming on and lots of the hands were wearing Labour Party badges. The foreman had called them up the day before and told them to take them off. Pat's eyes flashed. 'I wore mine the same as usual this morning, and when the old so-and-so pulled me up I told him where he got off. So he fired me – pronto.' She shrugged her shoulders. 'Might as well be now as later. They stick a notice in our pay envelopes every week warning us that if Labour goes in again we'll all be out on our ear! What the hell, the factory'll probably close altogether if the other side goes back.'

I asked her what she was going to do.

'I'm going up to my married sister, Alanda. She is always writing and asking me, and life on the farm can't be any worse than this hell-hole.'

I said I thought it would probably be much better. Then I asked her what was wrong with Sonny that he hadn't been to visit me lately.

She replied, 'I'm glad you asked me that, because I'm worried about him.'

'Why?' I asked rather apprehensively.

'Well, he's seldom home for tea. Gets out lively. Says he's sick of the wrangling that goes on at the tea table.'

'Yes, but why doesn't he come around here! Why, he hasn't been here for about two weeks.'

'Yes, why doesn't he, instead of getting around with the mob.'

'What mob?'

'Tony Elson's gang. Surely you've heard of them?'

I'd heard of them all right. Who hadn't? They were a bunch of larrikins in their teens who adorned the street corners every night.

Tony Elson, an undersized youth of about sixteen, was named the Wizard by the older members of the gang for his outstanding ability in organizing raids on Chinese gardens, and stealing poultry from backyards. He and his gang were always in some trouble or another with the police, what with petty thievery and molesting passers by. That was no company for Sonny.

'Listen, Pat! Do me a favour,' I said, after a while.

'Sure, what is it?'

'Tell him I want to see him urgently. He might come. Tell him my iron is broken, and I want him to fix it. Tell him anything you like as long as he comes.'

'Right. If anyone can manage him, you can, Caddie. I'm worried about him. Now, if it was Bill, I wouldn't care, but with Sonny it's different, isn't it?'

'Too right it is.'

Next evening Sonny came. He walked in just as I was finishing the dishes.

I smiled at him: 'You're a nice one – deserting a pal.'

'I haven't deserted you, Caddie,' he answered uncomfortably.

'Well, it's good to know that. Sit down.'

He seated himself down at one end of the table. I took the iron off the shelf and placed it before him. 'I don't know what's wrong with it . . . it won't heat.'

He pulled the iron towards him and asked for a screw driver, saying, 'It must have fused.'

I reached for the little box of odds and ends where I kept the screw driver, and placed it on the table, looking away from him, for I knew that nothing whatever was wrong with it.

After tinkering with it for a few minutes, he said: 'There's nothing the matter with it. I'll try it.' He stood on a chair, removed the light bulb, and plugged the lead into the light socket, for there were no power points in that house. Bending down, he ran his hand across the iron and, feeling its warmth, said, 'It's all right; you must have plugged it in wrongly.'

I thanked him, then suggested a cup of tea. I wanted to delay him so long that he'd miss going out to join the Elson's gang.

As I set the cup before him I said: 'Do you know what today is, Sonny?'

He looked at me, a frown on his face, 'Yes, it's Friday, isn't it?'

'Yes, of course it's Friday. But anything special?'

'Not that I know of.'

'You big dope. It's the twenty-fifth – your birthday.'

'Why, so it is. Getting old, aren't I?'

I laughed. 'You're a long way off getting old. Well, many happy returns of the day.'

He stopped munching and looked up at me. 'Thanks, Caddie. I'll bet no one else will remember it. They never do.'

I went inside and returned with a little parcel neatly wrapped in brown paper. I put it on the table in front of him.

He looked from the parcel to me. 'What's this?'

'Open it and find out.'

I leaned over his chair as he unwrapped it and lifted a book from the wrappings. He opened it. '*Barnaby Rudge* . . . by Charles Dickens. Gee, what a present! Thanks, Caddie.'

'You haven't read it, have you?'

He said 'No' he'd start on it that night.

'By the way, Sonny, how about you and me joining a lending library?'

'That's a good idea, but –'

I knew what was in his mind. He had no money.

'Perhaps I could join for both of us,' I said. Then, seeing he was about to object, added quickly: 'I could get four books at a time, you know. It would save you bothering about collecting them.'

'Just as you like, so long as you let me pay my whack.'

I knew he couldn't afford even this indulgence, so I said, 'Look, why be so damned independent? It's only a few pence . . . not worth worrying about.'

But he insisted. 'You have enough to do with your money.'

'Never mind about that, it can come out of my betting money. Sometime I might have a run of bad luck, then you can pay.'

'All right, if you insist.' He rose. 'I'd better be off now, Caddie.'

He left me assuring me that he would be burning the midnight oil.

'Come back tomorrow night and tell me all about it while I do some sewing,' I called after him.

'It's a promise,' he laughed.

Sonny came as promised the next night, but after that I did not see him again for several weeks. That decided me . . . I would have a talk with him about his associations with the gang. It was no business of mine, but I wanted so much to see Sonny make the grade. He was at that impulsive age when he might get into some bother with those corner larrikins.

When Sonny next called I was busy ironing. As he walked in through the back door I said: 'Hadn't you better throw your hat in first?'

He grinned as he sat down at the table, tucking his legs out of the way. Then he became serious. 'Caddie, I've come over to have a straight talk with you.'

'Shoot,' I said, wondering.

'Well, it's this way. People are talking. You know, the gossips.'

'The gossips? What have they been saying now?'

'Aw, they're saying things about you.'

'That's nothing; I'm used to that now.'

'But you don't understand. They're saying . . . er . . . well, er . . . you know, Caddie.'

'No, I don't.'

He shuffled his feet uncomfortably, twirling his hat on the table. 'It's me and Bill. Because we come here they say we're your boy-friends.'

'Well, of all the dirty swine! Why, you're only a kid. And Bill . . . why, it's awful.'

'I thought I'd better tell you, Caddie. I didn't want you to think I'd deserted you.'

'Oh, so that's why you haven't been near the place?'

'Yes, that's it.'

He went on to explain. 'It's not myself I'm worried about, it's you. You don't deserve that.'

I was indignant: 'Listen here. Between you and me I don't give a damn for any of them, so there. Please, Sonny, don't stay away on my account.'

Then to make it easier for him I went on flippantly, 'I can't say I'm not pleased at a bit of gossip like that; shows I'm not too dusty, eh? Haven't lost my sex appeal.'

He laughed. 'If you're sure you don't mind then I'll come again.'

44

I seemed the only one among my friends who was doing all right. There was more and more unemployment and the police began to make it tougher for those on the dole – on orders from above.

It always seemed ironical to me that there was money in beer and betting but none for a man wanting to do an honest day's work. Peter's letters reflected the same conditions in Greece.

Finally things reached such a state that not even Bill could make a go of it. So at last he rolled his swag and left to accept an offer from his elder sister's husband in the country to help with the harvesting. Pat had already joined her sister.

Dadda Sutton was always sick now, and spent the greater part of the time in bed. There wasn't much in life for this poor old man. There was very little pleasure in the home for him, especially now that Mumma Sutton had gone.

Sonny made my place a sort of second home. He enjoyed the comparative comfort and nice meals which he shared with us.

One evening, while we were playing a game of rummy, I asked: 'Sonny, how is Dadda these days?'

'He's pretty crook.'

'Do you think he needs a doctor?'·

'He won't let me call one – says he doesn't believe in 'em. Which reminds me, he told me to tell you that he would be round tomorrow, if he can make it.'

'What does he want to see me for?'

'Couldn't say,' he said, dealing out the cards.

I was curious, wondering what Dadda Sutton would want to visit me for, as he'd not been too cordial with me when I lived under his roof. I went to bed still puzzled over it.

Next morning he arrived, walking slowly down the side passage. I hurried out and helped him into the kitchen. He was almost bent double, and could scarcely stand.

I was shocked at his appearance. He was a dirty grey colour and had aged considerably since I'd last seen him – he'd always looked far older than his years. A black sateen handkerchief hung untidily about his neck, and his feet were only partly protected by a pair of old carpet slippers.

'You're very welcome, Dadda,' I said brightly. 'It's about time you paid me a visit. What about a cup of tea?'

He sat down panting.

'How are you, Dadda?' I asked.

'Not too good girlie; not too good,' he replied. He seemed to have a spasm and his face screwed up. 'It's me stummick. Must've eaten something that's upset me,' he explained.

I knew he wasn't right about that, for he'd suffered with his stomach ever since I'd known him.

'Sonny's very worried about you,' I said.

The old man shuffled his feet and said testily, 'Huh . . . worried about me – not likely.'

'He is. And he wants to get Doctor Dewey to give you an overhaul.'

He appeared not to notice my reference to the doctor, for he went on. 'Not one of 'em cares wot 'appens ter me.'

'I'm sure they do – all of them,' I protested. 'Why, only the other day I got a letter from Bill and he told me he was very worried about you. He reckoned it wasn't right for him to be away while you are not so good.'

'I don't mind him goin', if only Pat had stayed,' he said sadly. I knew Pat was his favourite.

Dadda stayed all the morning. He hadn't told me what he wanted to see me about.

As he was leaving I walked to the front door with him. He thanked me, then suddenly turned to me. 'You're a good girl. You was good to Mumma and you've been good to my boys, stuck to Sonny through thick an' thin.'

'I don't know what I'd have done without either of them,' I said very earnestly.

'What I reely came to see you about was this: I come to ask if I could come and live with you.' His voice trembled: 'It's so lonely now without Mumma and Pat.'

I hesitated. 'I haven't much room, Dadda.' I saw the pleading in his faded old eyes change to disappointment, so I added hastily: 'I think I can manage it at a pinch, Dadda. Come round tomorrow and I'll let you know.'

'God bless you, girlie, I know you will,' he mumbled, and shuffled out the gate and down the street.

I went inside and sat down to think things out. I decided that I'd do my best for the poor old man whom I felt was not long for this world.

That evening I told Sonny about his father's visit, and that I was going to take him in and look after him.

'But you can't very well do that, Caddie. You have enough to do now.'

'I've made up my mind to look after your father, Sonny,' I said with finality. 'Tell him to bring his things round tomorrow.'

'Thank you, Caddie.' He looked across at me with a soft expression on his face.

'I told him you thought he should have Doctor Dewey to look at him.'

'I suppose he hit the roof.'

'No, he didn't hit the roof. I'm afraid your father will never hit the roof again, Sonny. You know, he's an old man, and – I hate to say this – he's dying.'

'Do you really think so? I kind of thought he was, too.'

'Yes, I feel sure he is.'

Next day when Dadda Sutton called he said, in answer to my inquiry as to how he felt, 'I had a bad night, girlie.'

I told him he must go to bed at once. He murmured something about putting me to a lot of trouble, but I insisted. He let me order him around like a baby. It seemed odd that anyone could order Dadda Sutton around.

I fixed up Terry's room for him, putting Terry out in the dining-room to sleep on the settee. I fetched hot water and a towel for him to have a wash. Then he had a bowl of broth which I had prepared for him.

Sonny had promised to come over every day after he had done the rounds of job hunting. When I returned home late a few days later, Dadda was roaming about the house in his socks, his braces dangling, and Sonny was trying to persuade him to get back to bed.

'Dadda Sutton,' I said, bossily, 'what are you doing out of bed?'

He didn't appear to hear me.

As I neared him I saw a trail of blood on the floor. I gasped with horror, 'Oh, what's wrong, Dadda?'

'Don't be afraid, girlie . . . I've bled like this before and felt better for it.' He looked at me, attempting to reassure me. 'Somehow it always seems to give me relief.'

'Well, get into bed.' We helped him back to his room, Sonny on one side, me on the other.

'Get his pants off,' I said to Sonny. 'And as soon as you've done that fetch Doctor Dewey.' I hurried out to the kitchen to prepare some hot water.

When I went back to Dadda with a dish of hot water, I found him lying back on the pillows with his eyes closed, his face ashen. Had it not been for the rising and falling of the covers, I'd have thought him dead.

A little while and Sonny was back with the doctor. We both waited in the hall while the doctor went to Dadda. After a few minutes he reappeared. He looked at me and asked: 'What relation are you to the patient?'

'Just a friend, but this is his son,' indicating Sonny.

'I am afraid this is a hospital case; I'll call an ambulance,' he said as he left.

When the ambulance arrived I persuaded Sonny to stay at home while I went with Dadda to the hospital. Sonny seemed too bewildered at the sudden turn of events to be of much use.

On the way to the hospital Dadda opened his eyes and I bent over him. He asked me where we were, and I told him we were going to the hospital, and that the doctor said he wasn't to talk much.

'Oh!' said Dadda, and thought that over for a while. 'Look, girlie, would you go round to my place after, and git me pension book, and me watch? They're under me pillar.'

'All right, Dadda,' I said, 'I'll bring them to you tomorrow.'

After a long wait in the vestibule of the hospital, the matron came out. 'Are you Mr Sutton's daughter?' she asked me.

'No, a friend of the family.'

'Well, you'd better get in touch with his family as soon as possible. Explain to them that one of them must be here to sign the papers giving permission for the operation.'

So, it was as bad as that, I thought. Poor old Dadda!

'Is it very serious, matron?' I asked.

'It's very serious. Cancer always is,' she said, adding: 'Besides, he's no longer young, you know.'

I hurried home and broke it to Sonny. He sat quietly for a while, then said he'd better go up to the Post Office and put through a long distance call to his sisters and Bill, adding that he would go to the hospital and sign the necessary papers for the operation.

Next morning Sonny and I went to the hospital and waited while Dadda underwent the operation.

After a seemingly interminable wait, a nurse ushered us into a public ward where he lay. There was that sickening smell of ether fumes as we made our way behind the white screen which was drawn around the bed. Dadda lay there, a moan escaping his pale lips from time to time. His eyes opened and closed wearily. He didn't seem to notice Sonny as he leant over him.

Next day Bill and the two girls arrived. Each of the four showed their grief in their own way. I felt out of place standing there by the bedside and went to move away, but Sonny caught my hand and held it, drawing me back.

Dadda was dying. . . . After a while he opened his eyes; they were much clearer now, and they settled themselves on Pat. The expression in his eyes was a revelation: they seemed to caress her face, as he moved his head slowly from side to side. He was no longer able to speak, but he seemed to be trying to teil her with his eyes that she must not cry, when a tear from her face rolled down splashing his cheek.

I slipped outside.

It wasn't long after that Bill came out, blowing hard into his handkerchief. It was all over. Dadda Sutton was beyond all physical suffering now. Pat came out crying softly, Sonny's arm supporting her. Alanda, the other sister, followed, and she, too, was crying.

Bill made the final arrangements for his father's burial. There was no need to beg the undertakers to be allowed to pay off the cost by weekly instalments as they'd had to do for Mumma's funeral, for the Returned Soldiers' League came forward and paid all expenses, as Dadda had been a First World War veteran. A large Union Jack was placed over the casket as he was taken to his last resting-place.

Sonny decided to sell up the furniture in the home and move out. It would have been impossible for him to maintain the home on a dole ration and the few odd shillings which he sometimes managed to make doing odd jobs. He told me his plans. He was going on the track.*

When he broke the news to me I felt that it was Terry who was going away. I would miss Sonny after mothering him for so long.

'Are you going alone, Sonny?' I asked.

'No, Ron Skelton's going with me. You know him – my mate from school.'

I nodded.

'Decent sort of a cobber. Romped home with flying colours in his accountancy exams, but like me, he's never been able to crack it for a decent job.'

I felt relieved to know that Sonny had chosen Ron for his mate.

Sonny stood up and stretched his long limbs. 'Well, hooray, see you anon.' He went and closed the door quietly behind him.

When Sonny had disposed of the furniture he came straight to me and offered to pay me for little things I had done for him. I refused. How could I take it from him when he was going on the track with no certainty that he would get a job. I flatly refused. I wasn't in need now.

'Well, when I get a job, I'll square up with you then; and no knocking me back either,' he said.

* On the track—Tramping the back country in search of work.

Three weeks later I received a letter from Sonny. It was scribbled on a piece of white wrapping paper. It was to say that he was well, and that he and Ron had met and joined forces with a fellow named Red. Sonny explained that he was an old digger from the Great War, and I gathered he looked after the youngsters like a father. He was cook and chief scrounger, while Sonny and Ron did the chores. Sonny informed me that they were camping at the moment, sleeping under the stars. He warned me not to expect another letter for some time, as they would be moving camp in a few days, hoping to reach the nearest sheep station in time for the shearing on the chance of picking up a job.

After Sonny had gone, I got to thinking about everything, and what Bill had said about me being home and dried. But was I? I wondered. Anything could happen. What if I should get sick, and unable to work. Life was so uncertain.

45

Twelve months passed and the solicitor wrote to say that he hoped that my divorce would soon be finalized. I dropped in to see what 'soon' meant and found it was six months, a year. I was impatient at the delay but suddenly I thought, 'What does it matter? Peter's wife will never divorce him.'

One chapter of my life was being finished but I seemed as far off as ever from marrying Peter. I began to think I was doomed to bad luck. My husband had ceased to love me, and the man who loved me couldn't marry me! I was still full of gloom.

That afternoon when I went into the Ladies' Parlour to collect empty glasses, I noticed a woman sitting in a far corner. The parlour was dim at the best of times, so I switched on the light as I went over to her. I was about to ask her if she'd been waiting long when she turned her face towards me. The words died on my lips as I stared at her, not believing my own eyes. 'Esther!' I exclaimed. 'What are *you* doing here?'

'It's a small world, all right,' she said without answering my question.

I saw that she was ill. As I moved over to her she was suddenly seized with an awful bout of coughing.

'I'll get you a drink,' I said and hurried into the bar, and returned quickly with a double-header brandy. Esther had got over her spasm of coughing and was busy fumbling in her handbag for the money. She looked up.

I smiled back at her and thought it rather ludicrous that we should be smiling at one another. Rather, I thought, I should have been infuriated. But I think it was the sad state of her, her shabbiness, and her physical condition that had shocked me into feeling sorry for her.

I placed the drink before her, refusing to accept payment for it. When she insisted, I said, 'It's on the house.'

Sipping the brandy she told me that she'd contracted T.B. some years before, that she'd been twice in a sanatorium, and that John had left her years ago.

'Where are the children?' she asked me, turning her big dark eyes up to me. I told her about them briefly. She gave the ghost of a smile, saying, 'You're lucky!' Then she shuddered as though at some horrible memory and I waited for her to tell me more.

Just then a commotion from the bar distracted my attention. I left, calling back to her as I went: 'Don't go, I'll be back in a minute.'

A number of customers were waiting impatiently for service. I served them, and a few more came in, and when at last I returned to the parlour, Esther had vanished. I picked up the empty glass and went out into the yard and threw it into the burning embers of the incinerator.

I shall never know whether it was by accident that Esther found her way into that parlour, or whether she had discovered that I worked there and came to tell me she was sorry for what she had done to me, and then at the last moment funked it.

I couldn't get her out of my mind – her thin shabby figure, the worn face that had once been so beautiful. The shock of seeing her so changed made me look at myself with critical eyes. In the long mirror with its advertisement for soda water, I saw myself reflected, and for the first time I realized that the struggle for existence had begun to play havoc with my face and figure, too. Lines had come to stay around my eyes and mouth. I was beginning to put on weight, and bulged in the wrong places. I thought of the first day I had gone to work in a bar. What a different picture the mirror presented to me now!

I went home in a state of acute depression. That night I looked at the children, trying to see them as though they weren't my own.

Terry had turned thirteen and was a replica of his father, both in looks and build. So many of his ways reminded me of John. One of them was his lack of regard for money. Although he received a little more pocket-money than Ann, he borrowed frequently from her. Ann, now a leggy girl of ten, already showing signs of prettiness, was discussing just one such unsatisfactory transaction with him. I went over to the mantelpiece and took two moneyboxes from the shelf.

'Who owns this one?' I asked, shaking the heaviest one. I knew quite well to whom it belonged.

Ann answered, 'That's mine, Mummy.'

'Well!' I shook the other one in which a few coins rattled. 'And this is yours, Terry?'

Terry hung his head.

'You're not trying to save, and it will soon be Xmas,' I said.

Ann chimed in with: 'Yes, and I suppose he'll want to borrow off me again like he did last Xmas.'

Terry bristled. 'Huh, I won't ask you for a loan again, not ever,' he said emphatically. 'Anyway, you waste a fair bit on silly things like doll's shoes. What does a doll want shoes for? It can't walk.'

'That's enough, Terry,' I commanded. 'If you don't learn to save I will have to cut down on your pocket-money.'

'Aw, gee, Mum, a fellar can't make a do on it now. What would it be like if you cut it down? Why a fellar needs a couple of quid, not a couple of bob, to see him through.'

'Never mind all that slang, Terry, it isn't appreciated here,' I told him. Terry was changing; he tried to emulate his older mates, and already imagined he was grown-up and tried to get the last word with me.

He said, 'Well, at least I buy sensible things. What about that beaut slide-rule I bought, and those other drawing instruments?'

Ann attacked again, saying, 'Yes, but you borrowed some of the money from me to help buy them, that was last Xmas, and you haven't paid me back yet.'

'Go into the bedroom, Ann, and get my purse from the top drawer of my dressing-table,' I said.

She obeyed, leaving Terry and me alone for a few minutes.

'Now, Terry,' I said, 'I'm going to square up your debt to

Ann, then I expect you to manage on your allowance without borrowing. Do you hear that?'

'Yes, Mum,' he replied meekly.

Ann came back carrying my purse, which she handed to me, looking curiously at Terry, then at me.

'Now, how much does Terry owe you?'

'Four and ninepence, Mummy.'

'Well, here it is.' I handed her the full amount.

'Thank you, Mummy.' Taking her moneybox down from the shelf, she commenced dropping the coins into it, one by one.

Terry looked on in silence until she had finished, then shuffled his feet and, looking over at me said, 'Thanks, Mum.'

But it wouldn't be long before he became hopelessly involved in debt again. Terry just could not handle money. That was one of the things he'd inherited from his father along with his good looks. But he had a doggedness about work and capacity for love and loyalty his father never had.

Out of the blue came a letter from Peter: his wife had died unexpectedly: would I come to Athens and marry him? He couldn't possibly leave just as the business was getting on its feet again, particularly with his father an invalid. But he could send me the money for my fare and enough for me to put the children in a good school while I was away. By the time I reached him my divorce would be sure to be through, and even if it wasn't he couldn't bear to waste any more of our lives apart.

I was never so tempted in my life. Here was everything I'd ever dreamed of offered to me – a man who not only loved me and my children but who had been faithful to me for all the years of our separation. A man I could trust and respect and who would be the father my children lacked and needed. Terry's behaviour was showing me that more and more every day.

But I couldn't go. I daren't risk it. I talked it over with the solicitor, who warned me of the dangers if John should suddenly come to light and claim the custody of the children.

It was the kind of thing he would do – not because he wanted them but because of the kink in his character.

Was ever a woman so torn? I cried myself to sleep night after night as I tore up the blotched letters I couldn't bring myself to finish. I was starved for love; I was fed up of being the mainstay of our home; I was tired of being 'Caddie the barmaid', 'Caddie the S.P.'. I wanted to be Peter's wife. I wanted to have someone I could depend on forever.

But there was too much at stake for me to go. I wrote the letter at last. It was the hardest letter I ever wrote in my life.

46

After six months, my divorce was granted, and I had to wait another six months before I received my decree nisi and was given the sole and permanent custody of the children.

Then something happened that threatened to upset everything I'd worked for.

Paddy called to tell me he was giving up the betting. That was about all he said; Paddy didn't talk much. But later I learnt that he had become a registered bookmaker at Randwick, Sydney's world-famous racecourse.

Well, that was that! It meant I was once more on the outer. I knew I couldn't get a permanent job and I didn't know how we were going to live.

That night I couldn't sleep for thinking about it. Then all of a sudden it came to me, lying there in the gloom. I'd take up the betting myself the following Saturday. Of course, I hadn't enough capital to see me through even the first race unless I was lucky; but I'd take the risk.

So, when Saturday came around again I stood up as usual. My stomach commenced to play tricks on me as I awaited the results of the first race. Results were broadcast from a small mantel model set on a shelf in the bar. I lost. I panicked, knowing that if I couldn't meet my obligations I'd have to leave the district.

I think I lived a lifetime between that and the next race. I made endless mistakes – served the wrong drinks, gave wrong change. Finally a customer leant over the counter and told me off. 'Strike me dead, Caddie, but you're slipping! Why, only a minute ago I asked you for a pint and you gave me a glass . . . now when I ask for another pint, you give a man a whisky. Take the bloody stuff away,' he said, shoving the glass of whisky over to me. I apologized, assured him it wouldn't occur again and quickly served him with a pint.

When I heard the result of the second race I became a little easier. From then on, the goddess of fortune smiled on me, and at the close of the meeting, most of the favourites having won, I found myself on the right side of the ledger. I was home on the bit, as Bill would have said.

Yes, I was now an S.P. bookie in my own right. I was chasing the money from now on, making every post a winner. I was no longer battling for food and the bare necessities, but was making a bid for security.

I soon found I was making more money than in any job I could have taken on. But I didn't splash it about. I had other ideas in mind when I had a tidy little sock in the bank.

I kissed the liquor trade goodbye, but still continued on in the betting business, most of which was done by phone, which I managed to get connected early in the piece through a customer who worked in the Telephone Department at the G.P.O. I moved to a better house about two streets away.

The betting which had not proved easy at any time, when one took into account the constant vigilance needed to steer clear of the police, to say nothing of the various moods of my punters connected with the disputes over bets, was a thousand times more nerve-racking now I was out on my own. With Paddy in the background I'd never had to worry about where the money was coming from but now I used to get into a regular panic in case some outsider at long odds romped home, or one of the 'doubles' the boys were always trying to pick came off. But though I had my ups and downs, on the whole I kept out of trouble. It really seemed my luck had changed at last.

47

Peter's letter saying he was on the way back seemed proof of it. I was as excited as a young girl as I waited on the wharf for his boat to draw in. And as nervous! I was horribly conscious of the fact that I'd gone off a great deal in looks in the years he'd been away. All my frantic dieting to get some of the extra weight off before he arrived hadn't seemed to do much good.

As I stood on the wharf that sunny morning searching the side of the ship and watching the harbour, my mind went back to that first morning on Peter's balcony. What a different person I'd looked – and been – then!

As last I picked him out and realized with a shock that he was changed, too. I had a chance to observe him for a few minutes before he succeeded in picking me out among the crowd on the wharf.

He was thinner and looked much older – even at that distance I could see the lines on his face. And his hair was almost the colour of platinum! Then he saw me and smiled and it was the same Peter.

My legs were shaking as he came down the gangway towards me, looking more distinguished than ever.

I waited for the expectant look on his face to change to disappointment. But he just came up and put his arms round me and kissed me. Then he stood back, holding me by the shoulders and looked at me in amazement. 'Why, Caddie,' he said, 'you haven't changed at all, and look at me!'

I know you're always tempted to say you've never been so happy in your life when something particularly wonderful happens. But it was true of that home coming. Even now I can remember the scene round the table that night, with Peter sitting smiling at the children, and the two of them talking to him at once. They simply took him for granted. To Ann he was 'Daddy' and she sat on his knee and hugged him when he showed them the presents he had brought. To Terry he was the always-desired man-of-the-house and a friend in whom he had faith.

They were both full of excitement when he told them we were going to be married just as soon as he could get a licence.

'And in the meantime,' he said, 'I'm going to look for a flat or a house somewhere near the sea.' He paused and looked at me with a smile I'll never forget, 'And then we'll all live happily ever after!'

There was some technical delay over the licence but it didn't seem to matter. I had what I'd always wanted. A man whom I could trust absolutely, and whom I loved as I'd never loved John. Together we'd make a home that was a home. I'd live a normal happy life. Not many women, I thought, get security *and* happiness together

Three days before we were to be married, Peter suggested we should try out the new car he had bought and run up to the Blue Mountains for the day.

It was a wonderful spring day – the sunshine brilliant, the valleys full of blue mist, the wattle trees lining the roadway a mass of golden bloom. We drove as far as Katoomba, where we had tea, and at dusk we headed for home. I felt utterly happy as we sped down the winding road. All day we'd been catching up on the years we'd been apart. There were so many things one didn't put in letters. Now we were talking about our plans for the future – and what a future it was going to be!

We were about halfway down the mountains when we drove into a heavy mist which made it impossible to see more than a few yards of the road in front of us. We both fell silent as Peter kept his mind on the road ahead. As we neared Lapstone, a lorry coming in the opposite direction swung wide around the bend of the road, its glaring headlights trained on us. Peter swerved quickly to avoid it as it whizzed past. In a confused way I realized that something terrible was happening to us. The car crashed through a fence, its engine roaring as it toppled over an embankment, turning a complete somersault and finally landing on its wheels. The door nearest me flew open and I was thrown clear. Peter remained in his seat, slumped forward over the steering wheel.

The roaring, crashing sound ceased. There was silence. My face was wet with the soft falling mist as I lay there on the ground, my limbs numb. I called to Peter, but he did not answer. Then a feeling of nausea came over me and my mind slipped into unconsciousness.

We were taken to hospital in an ambulance, but Peter was dead on arrival.

After six weary months in hospital I was allowed to go home. It was Pat Sutton who came and took me back to her farm; and it was Pat who nursed me back to health again.

48

It was 1939. More than four years had passed since the accident when Peter was killed. Terry was nineteen, and was with a firm of architects in the city. Ann had completed a business course and was employed in a Government department. There were rumours of war in the papers.

I became afraid. What if war really came, they might take Terry from me. I tried to put the thought from me, but it persisted.

We were seated at dinner one evening when Terry got up and went over to the radio. After a few minutes fiddling with the dial he turned up the volume, and a foreign voice spoke.

'That's Berlin radio,' said Terry as he resumed his seat. After a few minutes of listening to the bombastic voice of the announcer, Terry looked across the table at me: 'There's going to be a big war. Don't believe the papers when they tell us that the German tanks are made of cardboard.'

'Oh, there won't be any war,' I told him. 'Get on with your tea, and stop worrying about those things.'

A few nights later Terry came home from work, his evening paper opened in front of him. 'Well, there you are. The Germans have invaded Poland.'

My heart seemed to stop. The papers had said that if Poland was attacked we would be at war. I had been too busy of late to bother about reading the papers, and this came as a shock. It was maddening. Just as I had got on my feet at last, this must happen. Terry would want to go.

Most mothers must have felt the same way the night when they sat by the radio and heard Mr Chamberlain announce to the nation that this country was now at war with Germany.

I was filled with dread. I was not interested in what happened to the Poles, or anyone else. All I cared was that they might take Terry away from me. I looked at him. He was pacing restlessly about the room; he did not want to talk. The room seemed stuffy. I rose and opened a window, and could hear shouting up the street.

'Listen to the newsboys,' I said for want of something to say. 'Come on.' I slipped an arm through Terry's and another through Ann's. 'Let's go up to the corner and buy the latest edition.' Without a word from Terry we walked up the street, and Terry crossed the road and bought a paper from a screaming newsboy. It contained nothing we had not already learned from the radio.

We went into the milk bar on the corner, and Mr Tipping came forward to serve us.

'Well, it's war, Mr Tipping. What do you think about it?' said Terry.

'Ah, they're always squabbling over there, Terry. It's got nothing to do with us, it'll blow over in a day or two, you see. Won't affect us at all.'

'Don't kid yourself, Mr Tipping, this will affect the whole world.' Terry was very serious. 'That fellar Hitler means business. Too many people get him mixed up with Charlie Chaplin.'

'Oh, we'll fix him in no time,' laughed Mr Tipping.

Terry looked at him pityingly as we walked out after having finished our drinks.

As we walked down the street, Terry stopped to talk to two youths who were standing outside a shop. When he caught up with us, I asked: 'Who were those fellows, Terry?'

'They're the Bennett boys. You remember them? I used to go to school with them.'

When we arrived home Ann took up her knitting and sat down on the lounge. Terry looked across at her and said, 'What's that you're knitting, Ann?' although he knew quite well it was a pullover for him.

'Your pullover, of course,' said Ann.

'Well, you had better undo it.'

'Whatever for?' I said, looking at him with dread.

'It's the wrong colour; it needs to be khaki.' He added, 'I'm going to the barracks tonight to enlist,' and he began pacing up and down the room as John used to do in the old days.

'Don't be absurd, Terry. Enlist indeed!'

He stopped pacing and looked at me. 'You'd better get used to the idea. I'm definitely going to enlist.'

With that he walked out of the house. I rushed after him but he hurried down the street, and I went back inside.

Ann and I sat down and looked at one another. Suddenly she jumped up and said what we wanted was a cup of tea. While she busied herself in the kitchen I went into a small room I called my 'Betting Office' and rang Victoria Barracks. The line was busy, but I kept on trying to raise them.

When a gruff voice finally answered, I said, 'Is that Victoria Barracks?'

The voice said it was.

'If a young man named Terry Marsh calls there to enlist, don't take him. He's under age. I'm his mother.'

The gruff voice chuckled, and hung up. I put the receiver back on the hook feeling foolish.

Ann and I waited up until Terry came home. He looked at me and said, 'You've won the first round.'

'Why, what do you mean?'

'They won't take me.'

'Why?' I asked, feeling elated.

'They're not ready to start enlisting anyone yet. But they will. The Bennett boys are going to enlist with me.'

I went to bed feeling smug in the belief that Terry would not be able to enlist. After all, I told myself, he was under twenty-one and I would have to sign the papers, and I certainly wouldn't do that. Let the Bennett boys go. Let them all go, but not my Terry.

The months passed and the Bennett boys sailed for overseas. Terry didn't sail with them. The Government had declared his work essential and his department would not allow him to enlist. He was furious and wrote dozens of letters and interviewed the heads of his department so many times that I began to fear they might get fed up with his pestering them and give their consent.

One night we received a visitor – in khaki. It was Sonny. Ann showed him into the lounge room. He came over to where I was standing and threw his arms around me, hugging me until I thought I'd break in two.

'Sonny, this is a surprise,' I gasped. I sat him down on the lounge and began scolding him for not writing.

'There wasn't much to write about, only the usual hard luck stuff. I didn't want to worry you with those things.'

He looked better than I had ever seen him. He was fatter, and the picture of health. I watched him as he took a khaki handkerchief from his pocket, and slipping the chin-strap from under his chin he put his slouch hat on a small table beside him, and began to wipe the perspiration from his face and neck.

'Where's Bill?' I asked.

'He's in it, too. He sailed about a month ago.'

'Well, he might have come to see me before he went,' I said indignantly.

'They left from Melbourne in a terrible hurry.

'How's Terry? No need to ask how you are, Ann,' he said jovially. Ann glanced up from her knitting and gave him a shy smile.

'Yes,' I said, smiling, 'she is quite grown-up now.'

'I'll say – and how!' His eyes were still on her face.

I said, 'You wouldn't know Terry now, why he's as tall as you are.

'I bet you could go a cup of tea, Sonny,' I asked, testing him on his old habit of never refusing a cup at any time.

'Too right, the stuff we get in camp is pretty crook.' He followed me out to the kitchen.

Sitting at the table over our tea, I asked: 'What made you join up, Sonny?'

'Why does anyone join up.'

'There are plenty of jobs now,' I persisted.

He shifted uneasily in his chair, 'But I've got a job!'

'Yes, but why not leave it to those who have had a good spin? Why, you've never had a decent job in your life; and now you want to go and fight. It's not your war, Sonny.'

He looked at me in astonishment. 'Well, I *am* surprised at you, Caddie! What if nobody went . . . where would we all be? Besides,' he added, 'it was good enough for my father to go in the last war, so it's good enough for me to go in this one.'

Sonny sailed shortly afterwards, and I never saw him again. Later I heard that he had been killed on Crete, and still later that Bill had been taken a prisoner by the Germans.

Then Japan came into the war. Terry was now twenty-one, and at last he had managed to get a clearance from his department. Within a week he had joined up.

It seemed to me, then, that there was to be no peace in my life. I was back from where I started. After battling and struggling for years, here I was facing, like mothers all over the world, the wreck of all my hopes.

I put the thought from me. Somehow I felt that Terry would come back. And I wasn't back to where I'd started from twenty years ago. The frightened young girl who had left her home because her marriage had broken up was gone. I had learnt a lot in those years. I could pull a beer with the best, and handle a crowded bar as though I had been born to it. Besides, I was a seasoned S.P. bookmaker . . . and I had faith in myself at last.

Postscript: Vale Caddie

In the years since Caddie's book was first published, she has become a legend. Letters come to me from all over the world, asking 'How is Caddie? What is she doing now?'

This year the same questions were asked me in Paris, Berlin and Moscow. Not long ago a woman wrote from Wales saying that Caddie's story had inspired her to write her own, and asking us both to stay with her in her little Welsh inn.

Caddie may be legend but her story is part of our rapidly changing history. With the new liquor laws the worst of our bad drinking habits have changed from the days when she was a barmaid.

In our affluent post-war society, those under thirty will read her struggle against poverty and unemployment as something far-off and perhaps incomprehensible. Not that we haven't pockets of misery in our boom-time country. Two years ago a group of civilian widows said to me: 'You should write about us. We are the Caddies of the Sixties.' And so she has given her name to the hard-working, underpaid women of today who battle amidst prosperity for the right to live and bring up their children on a miserly pittance.

I think of her as she wrote to me in 1954; from the home where she lived out her life near Penrith. *'I am writing this sitting on the verandah in the sun, and although it is late Autumn it is quite hot. The garden is full of chrysanthemums and a few late Easter daisies, and the vegetable patch is flourishing. The copy of CADDIE you air-mailed to me is on the table beside me. I cried when I opened it. I feel my life has been worthwhile.'*

Worthwhile, indeed! Who could ask more than to leave a book of lasting courage and a name that is a symbol of courage and humanity. And so Caddie lives on.